details to how historically, grains used to be malted, even though the overall general process is essentially the same.

In addition to the brewing and malting processes themselves, I decided to also describe the basics of beer classification during the 19th century that were used in contemporary literature, as well as a brief overview over the legislative side of beer: brewing in Bavaria was regulated by law, though not always strictly enforced. And while everyone is aware of the *Reinheitsgebot* (purity law) of 1516, more laws existed that had an influence on beer strength, ingredients, pricing and taxation. As one of Bavaria's most important foodstuffs, all these aspects of beer were of course part of the public discourse at the time, and deserve a closer documentation to give the reader more context.

Chapter 2

Bavarian Beer

For much of the 19th century, brewers in Bavaria were not free to brew beer as they pleased. Most the aspects of brewing were strictly regulated, whether it was the type of grain, the brewing ingredients overall, or even the beer's strength.

Generally, only barley could be generally used in brewing, wheat only under specific circumstances, and they had to be malted, as the only ingredients allowed were water, malt, hops and yeast. Any other ingredients, even entirely harmless fermentables like sugar, were completely prohibited.

The main types of beers that were brewed were *Braunbier* (brown beer) and *Weißbier* (white beer). *Braunbier* was always brewed from barley malt, while *Weißbier* could be brewed from either wheat malt, barley malt or a combination of two. Additionally, restrictions on brewing with wheat further complicated this matter. *Braunbier* and *Weißbier*, as their names suggest, were mainly distinguished by how the respective malts were made: for brown beer, malt was kilned at higher temperatures kilned compared to the malt for white beer, which was carefully kilned under very low heat, or sometimes even not kilned at all and only air-dried on a drying floor{}. The heat had an important impact on the browning of malt during the kilning process.

But the two types of beers were also fermented differently: in Bavaria, it was customary to ferment *Braunbier* under cold conditions and with a bottom-fermenting yeast only used for cold-fermented beers. *Weißbier* on the other hand was fermented at warmer temperatures with a top-fermenting brewer's yeast. These different types of yeast were simply known as *Unterhefe* (bottom yeast) and *Oberhefe* (top yeast). These names stem from how the yeast was harvested: *Unterhefe* from the bottom of the fermenter, *Oberhefe* from the top during fermentation. This process is called *top-cropping* in English. *Oberhefe* in Bavaria was also called *Weißbierhefe* (white beer yeast) due to its close association with white beer brewing.

As was found out only much later, the *Unterhefe* is distinctly different from regular brewer's yeast and has a genetic markup that was created through the hybridisation of brewer's yeast with a more cold-resistant wild yeast called *Saccharomyces eubayanus*. *Oberhefe* on the other hand is of the species *Saccharomyces cerevisae* and genetically very closely related to other top-fermenting brewer's yeasts, but the specific yeast used in Bavaria still shows some distinct properties, in particular in the aromas and flavours that it produces.

The different fermentation temperatures were also reflected in when each of these beers were brewed. Bottom-fermented beers could by law only be brewed from September 29 (the Christian festival of *Michaelmas*) to April 23 (*St. George's Day*), hence why the brown beer brewing season was often simply described as "von Michaeli bis Georgi" (*from Michaelmas until St George's Day*). This restriction had been in place since 1553 and was only abolished in 1868, at a time when fermentation and maturation cellars were already more advanced and often ice-cooled. Top-fermented *Weißbier* had no such restriction, and was often brewed during the summer.

Brown beer as a whole was also differentiated: by law, it could be brewed in two strengths. *Sommerbier* (summer beer; named after when it was served) or *Lagerbier* was brewed stronger (i.e. with more malt for the same amount of liquid) and underwent a lengthy cold maturation phase until it was eventually served during summer beer season. The opposite, *Winterbier*, often also called *Schenkbier*, was brewed at a lower strength, underwent only a brief cold maturation (if any at all), and was served during the winter season. Unlike the names might suggest, both beer types were strictly brewed only during the cold seasons, from September until April, as they were bottom-fermented beers.

White beer, as mentioned above, was also differentiated, but for another reason: this beer type could be brewed either from wheat malt or from barley malt. Brewing with barley malt had no particular restrictions, and thus brewing white beer was a quick way to brew inexpensive beer. Quick because the time from brewing to serving was much shorter compared to brown beer, often as little as 14 days to 4 weeks [1, p. 160], and inexpensive because the beers were typically brewed weaker and their production used less fuel. This made white barley beer a popular drink in the countryside that even poor people could afford as a refreshment.

Wilhelm IV., Duke of Bavaria

White wheat beer was pretty much the opposite though: in the Bavarian Code of Law that was enacted on April 23, 1516, the ingredients of beer were regulated so that only barley, hops and water could be used (yeast, although not mentioned, was known

Der Vierd tail

das söllhs den pfarrern in vnserm lannde nit gestatt werden sol/ausgenomen was die pfarrer vnd geystlichen von aigen weinwachssen habn̄/vnd für sich/jr pfarrgesellen/priester schafft vnnd hausgesynd/auch in der not den kindlpetterin/ vnd krannckhen leuten/vnnärlich geben/das mag jne gestatt werden. Doch geuätlicher weis/von schennckhens vnd gewins wegen/söllen sy khainen wein einlegen.

Wie das pier summer vnd winter auffm lannd sol geschennckt gepꝛawen werden.

Item Wir ordnen/setzen/vnnd wöllen/mit Rathe vnnser Lanndtschafft/das füran allennthalben in dem Fürstenthumb Bayrn̄/auf dem lannde/auch in vnsern Stettn̄ vnd Märckhten/da dessalhs hieuor kain sonndere ordnung ist/ von Michaelis bis auf Georij/ain maß oder ain kopf piers über ainen pfenning müncher werung/Vnd von sant Jörgen tag/bis auff Michaelis/die maß über zwen pfenning derselben werung/vnnd derennden der kopf ist/über drey haller/bey nachgesetzter Pene/nicht gegeben noch auf geschennckht sol werden. Wo auch ainer nit Mertzn̄/sonnder annder Pier pꝛawen/oder sonnst habn̄ würde/sol Er doch das/kains wegs höher, dan̄ die maß vmb ainen pfenning schennckhen/vnd verkauffen. Wir wöllen auch sonnderlichen/das füran allennthalbn̄ in vnsern Stettn̄/Märckhten/vnnd auf dem Lannde/zu kainem Pier/merer stuckh/ dann allain Gersten/hopffen/vnd wasser/genomen vnnd gepraucht sölle werden. Welher aber dise vnnsere ordnung wissenntlich überfarn̄ vnd nit hallten würde/dem sol von seiner gerichtzsobrigkait/dasselbig vas pier/zŭstraff vnnachläßlich/so offt es geschicht/genomen werden. Jedoch wo ain Geüwirt von ainem Pierprewen in vnnsern Stetten/ Märckhten/oder aufm lande/yezŭzeytn̄ ainen Emer piers/

Section "How the beer shall be served and brewed winter and summer in the country" in the Bavarian Code of Law of 1516

8

Das xxxvij blat

zwen oder drey/kauffen/vnd wider vnntter dem gemainen
Pawrssuolckh auffschennckhen würde/demselbenn allain/
aber sonnst nyemandts/sol die mase/oder der kopff piers/
vmb ainen haller höher dann oben gesetzt ist/zegeben/vnnd
aufzeschennckhen erlaubt vnd vnuerpotten sein.

Von Newen vnd vngewöndlichen Prewheüsern vnd Tafernen.

Wir wöllen auch/das die Neüwen Prewheüser/vnd Ta-
fern/so vor allter nit Prewheüser/noch Tafern gewest
sein/vnd den Stetten/Märckhten/vnd anndern Lannd-
säffen/zu nachtail vnnd schmelerung/von Neüwen aufgericht sind/gar vnd gantz abgethan/vnd füran kains wegs
gestatt werden/söllen.

Es wäre dann/das ain Prewhause/von dem Prelaten/
Edlman/oder Hofmarchhertn/zu notturfft seins closters/
oder gesäss/neüwes aufgericht würde/das sol jnen zu jrm
geprauch zügelassen sein.

Wo auch nit Edlmans gesäss/vnd doch Tafern daselbs
wärn/die vor allter die Prewheüser nit gehabt/vnd diesel-
ben Prewheüser innerhalb zehen jarn aufgericht wärn/die
selben söllen auch abgethan/vnd hinfüran auzürichten/nit
mer gestatt werden.

G

"How the beer shall be served and brewed winter and summer in the country" continued and used as fermentation agent but was not seen as an ingredient as such). This was not an explicit ban of using wheat in brewing, but rather an implicit one. Only in 1567, Duke Albrecht V. enacted a mandate that allowed brewing with wheat only if you grew the wheat yourself or bought and imported it from outside Bavaria. It also limited serving white wheat beer to the regions north of the river Danube up to the Bohemian Forest. Building new white beer breweries was also banned. The reason the duke gave was that white beer was "a useless drink that doesn't nourish you, doesn't give you strength or power, and makes those who drink only want to drink more of it."

This mandate was relatively poorly enforced. In a document from 1599, 20 white beer breweries were listed in Lower Bavaria. Only the brew houses of two noble families, the Barons of Degenberg and the Counts of Schwarzenberg, had an explicit right to brew white beer, while others could at most claim a customary right.

Coat of Arms of Degenberg

The Degenberg's brewing privileges were awarded to Hans VI. of Degenberg and his male descendants by Wilhelm IV. on 3 August 1548 to brew and sell white beer in the area north of the Danube up to the Bohemian Forest. The Schwarzenberg family were in turn given the right to brew for them and their male descendants in 14 June 1586, to brew white beer in their brew house in Winzer and to sell it in the Duchy of Bavaria. A few communal brew houses in Lower Bavaria were also traditionally brewing white beers, but their rights were unaffected at the time.

The Degenberg family line went extinct with the death of Hans VIII. Sigmund of Degenberg on 10 June 1602. In the Schwarzenberg privilege, the Wittelsbacher family, which were the rulers of Bavaria at the time, had secured the right for themselves that if the Degenberg family line ended, the Wittelsbacher in turn would receive the right to brew white beer. Duke Maximilian I. seized that chance and started paying the salaries at the Degenberger breweries from 1 August 1602 to ensure continued production of white beer, even though the Wittelsbacher did not yet own the brewery. Settling the inheritance took a while, but on 26 February 1607, a contract was signed that the heirs of the Degenberg family, the Barons of Closen, would sell the Degenberg breweries to the Wittelsbacher family for 82,000 Gulden, while in turn, an old debt over 20,000 Gulden from a 1488 inheritance contract between the Degenberger and the Wittelsbacher was cancelled. The 1488 contract stated that if the Degenberg family line ended, the Wittelsbacher family was to be paid 20,000 Gulden.

While white beer and its brewing was criticised in the 1605 and 1612 sessions of the Bavarian Parliament as wasteful, unhealthy and potentially causing bad harvests in the future, Maximilian I. dismissed any such concerns, pointing out that any wheat used for brewing was imported, and that in places in which white beer was brewed and consumed, in particular Bohemia and Upper Palatinate, people did not get sick or die more often than in Bavaria.

Maximilian I., Duke of Bavaria

This all set the foundation for establishing a state monopoly on white wheat beer in Bavaria that was further supported by establishing a relatively tight network of state-owned white beer breweries all over Bavaria. By 1612, nine white beer breweries were already owned by the state, and further nine communal brew houses could be made liable to pay a levy.

The brew houses in Zwiesel, Schwarzach and Linden were previously owned by the Degenberger family and were run by the Wittelsbacher from August 1602 onwards. Another brew house in Gossersdorf that had only recently been opened in 1600 was sold to Maximilian I. in November 1602. By that time, the brewing privilege of the Schwarzenberg family was basically forgotten in Munich, but when Wolf Jakob of Schwarzenberg could provide an original copy to the court chamber, Maximilian I. decided to buy out the Schwarzenberg family and take over their brewery in Winzer on 29 April 1603.

The beginning of the white brew house in Munich can be dated to 16 October 1602, when white beer was first sold from the Ducal cellar. For these initial brews, the brewer Sigmund Lettl and brewmaster Peter Wolf, both from the Schwarzach brewery, had been ordered to Munich, to teach the brewers at *Hofbräuhaus* how to brew white beer, until a dedicated brewmaster, Hans Amman, was hired. In January 1607, a separate white brew house was built.

Other white brew houses that were established were in Mattighofen, where the brown brew house was converted to a white brew house in 1607, in Kelheim, where a new white brew house was built starting summer 1607 so that beer could be brewed from April 1608, and Traunstein, where an existing building was bought and remodelled as a white beer brewery in 1611.

As mentioned above, nine communal brew houses that were brewing white beer were made to share their revenue with the Duke. These included the breweries in Viechtach, Regen, Kötzting, Furth im Wald, Neukirchen bei Hl. Blut, Eschlkam, Schönberg, Grafenau and Hals. In later years, Maximilian I. slowly further consolidated his network of breweries [2, pp. 46–83].

One specific type of speciality beer specifically brewed in Munich was *Bock*. It was a strong *Lagerbier* brewed with about 1/3 more malt, but with less hops. *Bockbier* was allegedly only brewed in December and January, after which it had to mature for at least 3 months, until it was finally tapped in the month of May [3, p. 260].

The origins of *Bockbier* actually lie in a beer brewing crisis: from September 1571 onward, brewing brown beer was completely banned and was only partially lifted in 1580. During this time, the Bavarian duke had beer from Zschopau, Saxony delivered to the court, and the Nuremberg trading house *Unterholzer* also facilitated the delivery of *Ainpöckischpier* from Einbeck from 1573 until 1589. The court servants received their beer from the breweries of the Franciscan and Augustinian religious orders, or from the brewer Georg Mänhart, who bore the title "Hofbräuer" (court brewer) because of it. These Munich brewers received specially alloted portions of grain from the ducal storehouse with the order to brew and deliver a specific amount of beer of the best quality to the court.

In 1589, the court initiated its own brewing operations, the *Hofbräuhaus*, though building works only commenced in 1591. When the brew-house started operations, Mänhart of course lost business and fell into poverty, so he received an annual payment of 100 Gulden as compensation. In 1614, the *Hofbräuhaus* started brewing their own version of the strong *Doppelbier* from Einbeck, and since the result was of the same quality as the original, further orders from Einbeck were cancelled [4, pp. 15–17].

An even stronger "luxury" beer was *Salvatorbier*. It was originally only brewed by monks of the Paulaner order, presumably only for their own nourishment. In 1751 the monks received an official permit to serve beer. As part of the secularization of Bavaria, the Paulaner monastery in Neudeck was closed down, In 1806,

Franz Xaver Zacherl purchased the former monastery brewery and resumed brewing there, including *Salvatorbier*. Until 1848, it was exclusively brewed at Zacherl's brewery, and only served for 6 days every year from the beginning of April [3, pp. 260–261]. When all the luxury beer privileges were abolished in 1848, other local breweries also started picking up brewing this type of beer, until in the late 19th century, Zacherl's brewery reclaimed the exclusive rights to the name *Salvator* in a series of lawsuits.

In terms of beer legislation, the Bavarian Code of Law of 1516 was a harmonisation and clarification of other previous legislation that regulated beer ingredients and prices, but it did not necessarily supersede local regulations in cities and market towns. In Nuremberg, the use of barley as the only grain permitted in brewing was regulated as early as 1303. Later on, more beer-related legislation was codified, such as recipes, brewing process and pricing, and remained in law until economic liberty was introduced in 1806. In Eichstätt, the prince-bishop introduced a law that only allowed barley, hops and water for brewing. In Munich, the city council regulated the permitted beer ingredients to only be barley, hops and water, much like the later law of 1516. This regulation was re-enacted in 1487 by Duke Albrecht IV., initially for Munich but later also for Upper Bavaria. In Regensburg, the local city council regulated in 1469 that only barley malt, hops and water could be used in beer brewing. Similarly, the prince-bishop of Bamberg introduced a law that only allowed malt, hops and water for brewing. The Duke in Bavaria-Landshut regulated in 1493 that brewers were only allowed to use malt, hops and water "to avoid punishment on body and property." This multitude of local laws and regulated was what necessitated a harmonisation for all of Bavaria. Nowadays, the law of 1516, but also the other preceding local laws, are often called "Reinheitsgebot", or "purity law" in English, but this term was only coined in 1918.

The exact reason why such regulations were seen as necessary is not known, but a number of theories have been brought forward: the regulation of grains helped secure the availability of food in case of crop failure. The regulation of hops as the only preservative may have had to do with a prohibition of other psychoactive ingredients or to even suppress remnants of pre-Christian ritual herbs.

The law of 1516 itself in its strictest interpretation was only valid for a relatively short period, as a ducal decree of 1551 permitted the use of coriander and bay leaves and explicitly prohibited certain other herbs, while the Bavarian Code of Law of 1616 also allowed salt, juniper berries and caraway seeds in reasonable amounts as ingredients, while other harmful herbs or seeds like henbane were explicitly banned [5, p. 158].

Even though brewing rights for the intention of selling the beer were limited in Bavaria to a certain extent, *home-brewing* strictly for consuming the beer in your own house was still permitted in Bavarian State Regulations of 1553 and 1616 [5, pp. 25–26]. This included also serving beer to your housemaids and servants, as well as the brewing rights for the clergy's own use, while monasteries were specifically banned from running taverns within their own walls, or selling wine from their cellars [5, pp. 73–74]. Selling home-brewed beer was still punishable by law, including the seizure of the beer. Due to the concern of tax fraud and the fact that only few families actually had the need to brew so much beer for themselves that warranted building their own brew-house, home-brewing was eventually banned in Bavaria, unless houseowners has a special authorisation from the sovereign, as written down in the Bavarian Civil Code of 1756 [5, pp. 25–27].

Generally, Bavarians were not free to trade in beer as they pleased: in an order from 25 January 1628, they were prohibited from importing foreign beer, as well as going abroad to consume in foreign inns. This was punished with confiscation in the former case, or a fine in the latter case. Court clerks, customs officers and toll collectors were ordered to especially pay attention to illegal imports, and were even allowed to visit cities and market towns in case of a suspicion. When a fine was ordered, these officials received a third of it, and thus it was in their own best interest to enforce this ban [5, pp. 85–86].

In addition to that, Bavaria had several degrees of limitations of who was allowed to buy beer from where. The oldest limitation was that no beer could be brought into cities and *Bannmärkte* (market towns with their own court) unless it was from the city's or town's court district. There were only few exceptions to this: when all the local *Sommerbier* was already finished before Michaelmas, beer could be imported until the *Schenkbier* started being tapped. This happened quite often in Munich, where *Märzenbier* from Tölz was frequently imported. Another exception was the import of beer by free people for the own consumption, while for people under Bavarian serfdom, such imports were still banned [5, pp. 87–88].

Another common type of purchasing limitations were so-called *Notwirte*, a type of innkeeper who by law was forced to purchase any beer from a particular brew house and was not allowed to buy beer from any other brewery (except for white wheat beer). This was introduced to the advantage of owners of large breweries in the 18th century. Innkeepers were either assigned by the local ruler to a brewery, or assigned to a brewery by jurisdiction, and the inn or tavern was legally obliged to buy their beer from the respective brewery as long as the beer was of acceptable quality and had the correct strength [5, pp. 89–100].

In the late 18th and early 19th century, the prince-elector of Bavaria, Maximilian I. Joseph, worked on reforming many of the business regulations. Naturally, this also affected beer and brewing. He ended compulsory beer purchases, where landlords of pubs and inns had to buy locally brewed beer, in 1799, by declaring all existing beer purchase contracts null and void. Landlords now had more freedom to purchase beer. On the same note, the *Märzenbierlosung* was also ended. Under this regulation, local breweries had to draw lots when they were allowed to sell their beer after the end of brewing season. At most three breweries were allowed to sell at the same time. By removing this regulation, brewing businesses could develop more freely and actually grow and for the first time, were able to compete on quality instead of being forced to sell their beer only at certain times during the year.

Taxation also changed: the tax on beer and distilled spirits, previously charged on the liquid itself, was replaced with a tax on the malt itself, the *Malzaufschlag* (lit. *malt surcharge*). Even though the malt tax rate itself was about half of the old beer tax, the malt tax revenue in 1806/07 was twice the amount of previous years. This was mainly attributed to the increased productivity and production output of breweries, but could partially also be explained through a reduction in beer- and brewing-related tax evasion overall.

Prince-elector and later King of Bavaria, Maximilian I. Joseph

The reformations of 1806 were again revised in 1811, in the so-called *Biersatzregulativ* (lit. *beer rate regulation*), which was designed to ensure a consumer protection from beer that was too weak, unhealthy or too expensive, while also securing sufficient tax revenue for the state and revenue for the breweries. For that, specific recipes for beer types were mandated: from a Scheffel of malt, at most 7 Eimer of *Schenkbier* or 6 Eimer of *Lagerbier* could be brewed. For *Schenkbier*, 3 Pfund of hops had to be used, while for *Lagerbier*, it was 5 Pfund hops. The price for the beer to be sold was also regulated by setting a maximum amount for the *Ganterpreis*, which was how much the brewer could charge at most for his beer to a pub landlord. Pubs and inns were also bound by a *Schankpreis*, which was the final price for which they had to sell to consumers. This price was 2 *Pfennig* higher than the wholesale price at the location where the beer was sold to consumers. The specific price composition took into account that some costs were more or less fixed every brewing season, while others, in particular barley and hops, varied season by season. In total, it ensured a fairly predictable maximum pricing for breweries, pubs and consumers. As the *Ganterpreis* was set locally, pubs could increase their profits by buying beer at places where the wholesale price was cheaper, and then sell this beer at the local *Schankpreis*.

Initially, brewers feared this new regulation as they assumed it would cut into their profits, but after 10 years, overall satisfaction was high as the calculations for brewers became simpler and more predictable. It even secured the existence of relatively small, manual breweries despite the increased competition from country-side breweries [6, pp. 26–38].

When it came to the ingredients used in beer brewing, Bavaria is generally associated with being very particular about it. As already mentioned earlier, the specific ingredients allowed in brewing beer had been regulated by law and ducal decrees several times. At the end of the 18th century and the early 19th century, there were certain aspects about brewing ingredients that were discussed in legal literature.

Unlike what is often being suggested today, the question of whether grains needed to be malted in order to be used for brewing was not central until 1806, when beer taxation changed from a fixed tax on beer itself to a taxation of the malt itself at the time when it was crushed for brewing.

A very real health concern was the intentional or unintentional adulteration of grains, whether it was seeds of *Lolium temulentum* (poison darnel or cockle), a plant often infected with a fungus that produces neurotoxic indole alkaloids, or ergot, a fungus

Map of the Kingdom of Bavaria, 1808 [7]

affecting certain grains that contains relatively large amounts of ergotamine, a psychotropic substance [5, pp. 148–149].

Through practical experience, brewers had already recognised that soft water was better suited to brewing than hard water. The means through which some brewers tried to soften their brewing water were questionable, though: some tried to mix in cow dung, while others added buckets of ash lye which not only added a certain taste to the beer but was said to also cause illnesses. It was thus suggested to completely ban the use of "foul water" in brewing, or if nothing else was available, that brewers at the very least had to filter their brewing water through layers of sand. Alternatively, brewers should try to soften their water through boiling [5, pp. 149–150].

With regards to hops, there were two main concerns related to the purity: first, there were brewers who used ingredients other than hops to give the beer bitterness, a specific taste or an intoxicating strength. The concern here was mainly whether the ingredients were poisonous or otherwise detrimental to people's health, so low amounts of harmless ingredients were acceptable to a certain extent, but police were nevertheless told to be alert about any potentially harmful additions. The second concern was the adulteration of imported, expensive hops with cheaper, locally grown hops. During the 18th and early 19th century, Bohemian hops were preferred to Bavarian-grown hops, and while Bavarian hops became moderately successful to prevent an egress of currency to a foreign country, they were also used by some fraudulent hop traders to cut imported hops. On 24 January 1767, the privy council of Bavaria enacted a resolution that banned the purchase of Bavarian country-side-grown hops unless the purchaser owned a brewery. This was not only to prevent a fraudulent cutting of Bohemian and Bavarian hops, but also an unnecessary increase in the price of Bavarian country-side hops [5, pp. 152–154].

Beer faults, such as hazy or sour beer, were also an issue at the time. Fixing hazy beer was relatively simple: brewers added isinglass to the beer or added beaten egg-whites or calves' trotters to the boiling wort to clarify it. These methods seemed to have been allowed and were considered harmless, but were still thought to be a source of beer taking on a peculiar flavour and going off more quickly. Sour beer on the other hand was often caused by not adding enough hops to the beer in the first place, by not boiling the wort thoroughly, by not having cool, clean cellars, or by simply having very hot weather. Some brewers and inn-keepers try to hide the acid in the beer through various means, such as adding lye, pot ash or quicklime, all of which were actively harmful to beer drinkers. In the past, a superstitious method to supposedly "fix" a sour beer was to hang a thief's thumb into the beer, a method that was also considered harmful. Some brewers also added salt to the beer, another prohibited and punishable adulteration that was meant to make beer drinkers thirstier [5, pp. 156–157].

By the end of the 19th century, the ideas of what was specifically allowed and prohibited in beer brewing in Bavaria had further solidified. The Bavarian *Malzaufschlaggesetz* (lit. *Malt Taxation Law*) of 1868 specifically said in Article 7 that it was prohibited to use any additions and surrogates instead of malt, no matter whether it was unmalted grains, a blend of malt and unmalted grains, or anything else, and that brown beer could only be brewed from barley. Beer that was brewed using surrogates like unmalted grains, starch, sugar, syrup or molasses were considered fraud both against the state, as it was defrauded of malt tax that would have otherwise been paid, and consumers, as the produced alcohol beverage was legally not beer in Bavaria [8, pp. 3–4].

Caramel colouring, used to darken beer, was equally banned, even though it did not actually add any fermentable extract to the beer. From a health perspective, no issue was seen why it couldn't be used, but from purely legal perspective, the only way of efficiently darkening beer was brewing it with roasted malt [8, pp. 15–18].

In terms of hop surrogates, some poisonous surrogates were allegedly used, but brewers generally were using hops, as surrogates had no preservative effect unlike hops. Using poisonous surrogates would also have been a crime against the health of their own customers [8, pp. 4–5].

When it came to preserving beer for export, methods like carbonisation or pasteurisation were allowed, as they did not add or remove any of the matter or their ratios that were part of the beer through its production process. The application of other ingredients, like salicylic acid and calcium bisulfite, as preservatives on the other hand was banned, as they were not contained at all in the original brewing ingredients, while adding alcohol as preservative would make the beer stronger than brewed naturally [8, p. 7].

Chapter 3

Malting

3.1 Benno Scharl (1814)

The *Weiche* (a vessel to steep grains) is first filled with water, to which the barley grains are then added. The amount of water needs to be just so that all barley is fully submerged and any impurities and dead kernels can float to the surface. Anything that is floating on the surface is pushed back down five or six times every half hour. Anything that still floats after 6 hours of steeping can be skimmed off. After about 24 hours, the water is drained and new, fresh water is added. This is repeated at least 3 times, especially in warm weather, to prevent the grains from taking on a bad smell.

The amount of steeping time depends on the barley's dryness. Freshly harvested barley can be steeped for just 1.5 to 2 days, while barley that has been dried for longer and stored for 2 to 3 months requires 3 to 4 days of steeping, especially in cold weather.

An indicator when the barley has been sufficiently steeped is when you try to bend a single grain over your thumbnail, it doesn't break anymore, or alternatively, if you squeeze a grain between your fingers from both pointy ends until it gets crushed it doesn't hurt your fingers. Insufficiently steeped barley cannot be fully crushed up by hand. At the same time, it is better to steep barley a little less than too much, to ensure it will later grow more uniformly.

When the barley has been steeped sufficiently, all the water is drained and the barley is transferred to the malting floor, called *Wachstenne* (lit. *growing floor*) or *Haufentenne* (lit. *heap floor*) and spread out thinly so that it can dry for some time. After 5 to 6 hours, the barley needs to be turned (*widern* in German). This is then repeated every 6 hours until the grains start germinating. When the weather is warmer, this can also be done more often, while the barley should not be heaped higher than a foot.

When it's colder, 56 °C or even cooler, the barley needs to be heaped up as soon as it's germinating, and depending on the temperature, the size of the heap needs to be varied. The grains are then left heaped until the grains under the surface start to "sweat", i.e. form condensation on the surface. Then it's time for the heap to be turned. This needs to be done in a particular way in which the heap is divided into three horizontal layers: the first (top) layer is shovelled "to the middle", the second (middle) layer is shovelled and thrown up so that it spreads out more, and the third (bottom) layer is again shovelled "in the middle". The author unfortunately does not clarify what "to the middle" or "in the middle" mean. This turning process needs to be done at least 4 times, until the grains have grown sufficiently.

When done properly, this should ensure that most if not all grains have germinated and grown. This is also dependent on the specific harvest: in some years, of 1000 grains not a single ungerminated one can be found, while in other years, up to 10% of all grains remain ungerminated. Malt that hasn't germinated properly is seen as an issue why beers later won't properly clear up.

Another influence is the water: with some water sources, the grains only need to grow short, while for others, they need to grow longer to ensure that the beer brewed from it will later clear up. This is something where the head brewer of a brewery needs to have experience how to do it best with the water source they have available. Generally though, it is better to let the grain grow shorter, to prevent too much of the starch to be converted to sugar when the rootlets have grown too long.

The malting process forms the foundation of a good beer. It not only has to be done diligently, but also needs to be well-timed. The first turning can never be damaging and can't be done too often. But not turning often enough can cause damage to the grains when the top layer dries out but the layers underneath remain wet. This would cause very uneven growth.

But it is even more damaging when the grains are already germinating and are then not turned at the right time. It then needs to be ensured that the grains don't lose too much of their "sweat" as that would slow down further growth. Care needs to be taken of that when turning the grains, and they must not be thrown up too high during that time.

What's even worse than that though is not to turn the grains at all: the heap of grain get warm, and the grains in the middle start growing quicker than the grains on top and bottom. Due to the higher temperature, the grains also start fermenting which gives the malt an unpleasant smell. Beer made from such malt will not taste good and will go sour quickly.

The temperature of the malt heap when it is first turned should ideally be 25°C. When it is turned the last time, it can easily have an internal temperature of 32°C, but it shouldn't go warmer than that.

When the malt has grown sufficiently on the malting floor, it is brought to a drying floor, the *Welke* or *Schwelge*. That's where the malt is meant to dry before it can be kilned.

The work that is required on the *Welke* is that it needs to be regularly turned, every 4 to 5 hours, especially on the first day when the malt is still relatively wet from the malting floor. If it remains unturned for too long, it can again heat up internally, especially on warmer days, and resume growing, but rather on the acrospire than the rootlets, which is especially damaging to the malt. If the acrospire has grown longer than half an inch from the grain, it is unusable for brewing as it has depleted its starches. The malt needs to be turned at least 6 times before it is kilned, and should not be wet on the surface as that would cause it to take on a bad smell.

The malt is kilned not at all at once, but rather in 3 to 4 batches, starting with the malt that has already sufficiently dried. The first batches will likely be smaller, while the final batch will likely be larger as more of the malt has dried well enough.

As soon as the malt is on the kiln, it is fired up and the heat is directed to the kiln. After an hour, the malt is turned for the first time to ensure that grains that were previously on the bottom are now at the top and vice versa. This needs to be repeated every 30 to 45 minutes so that the malt is kilned evenly. The maximum temperature at this stage should be no more than 70°C. If it gets hotter than that, the malt can easily burn. Beer from such malt will have an unpleasantly rough taste and will lose some of the starch, especially if the malt has been turned insufficiently. The beer will receive its colour from the malt, and therefore it needs to be ensured that the malt is turned often enough to all get the same colour. This requires diligent work.

When some of the malt seems like it's kilned well enough, the fire needs to be turned down and the malt needs to be turned another 4 to 5 times. To check whether a malt has been kilned sufficiently, the following tests can be applied: when biting into a kernel, it should crack like the crunchy crust of a freshly baked bread roll, while the inside of the malt kernel needs to be white like wheat flour and can also be used like chalk to leave a mark on the wall.

Bad malt, which is called *Steinmalz* (lit. *stone malt*) or burnt malt, can be recognised by trying to bite on it, for it is as hard as stone. There can be many reasons for this:

1. if the barley is growing for too long on the field, or is brought into storage in a bad state.
2. if it heats up during storage.
3. if it turns bad due to moisture, such as rain.
4. if it gets over-steeped in the *Weiche*.
5. if the malt heap is left unturned for too long and heats up too much.
6. if the same happens during drying.
7. if the malt is not dry enough when put on the kiln.

The second way of kilned malt going bad is if it isn't turned often enough while on the kiln, so that too many kernels remain on the bottom for too long and thus burn. When biting into such a kernel, the inside has turned into a brown-black coarse, semolina-like powder instead of being white.

When all the malt has been kilned sufficiently, it is removed from the kiln and stored in the malt box. This box needs to be clean, dry, have some air holes but at the same time need to be closed well enough so that no pigeons or other birds can get into the box.

When the malt is added to the box, it should be spread out over the whole length, but when malt is removed for conditioning and crushing, a section of it shall be taken that goes across several batches of kilned malt. This way, the beer should always keep the same colour even if different batches of malt have attained different colours during kilning.

Ideally, malt shouldn't be used immediately for brewing. Instead, it shall be left to rest for 2 months in the box so that it can reabsorb some moisture from the air which not only increases its volume, but also makes it easier to dissolve in water later.

If malt is made for the next brew year, the germ shall be left on the malt and only be removed closer to the brewing date.

(Source: [9, p. 83])

3.2 Johann Albert Joseph Seifert (1818)

Barley is added to the steeping vessel (*Einweichkuffe*), then water is poured over it. Initially, this is for cleaning the barley, so the dirty water is drained and replaced with fresh water several times. Any unsuitable barley kernels float to the top and can be skimmed off.

The exact time how long the barley needs to steep can't be simply determined in hours. It depends on the temperature, the dryness of the barley, whether hard or soft water is used, and other factors. The author recommends using river water, rain water or other soft water, and only so much that there is still one hand's width between the barley and the water surface. The barley should be stirred and the water replaced when it's dirty until the barley has been properly cleaned. Then the barley is left to steep. Any water that has been soaked up by the kernels is refilled so that the grains are always fully covered by water.

After 24 hours, the water is completely drained and new water is added. This is repeated every 24 hours until the barley has the following properties:

- it needs to be crushable between thumb and index finger on both pointy ends. That should not be sore to your fingers.
- the husk shall be easily separable from the endosperm.
- the grain still needs to be hard enough that, when cut or bitten open, it shall be usable to write on wood planks.

When this has been achieved, it is then immediately moved to a stone or wood floor where it then shall grow. If the barley steeps for too long, it can attain some acidity which will later be noticeable as a rough taste in the final beer.

The barley is heaped up, and if it's cold, covered with sacks. Whether to use stone or wood floors is something that the brewer needs to find out, but the author recommends stone floors during the summer as they cool better, and wooden floors during the winter as they keep the heat better.

The barley is then kept heaped up until, when sticking in your hand, it feels quite warm. This should usually happen within 24 hours, with warm weather even quicker. This heating up requires the attention of the brewer, as it initiates the germination of the grain which will first grow three small rootlets. If it is too hot, a blade of grass could also form. If this happens, then the barley is unusable for brewing. The rootlets have an unpleasant taste, and will eventually have to be removed from the grain itself.

The promote an even growth, the heap of barley is getting turned as soon as a small rootlet can be seen. Turning too often can be damaging, as it can cause uneven growth. When the rootlets are about twice as long as the grain, this work step is finished and the malt needs to be dried with air, though not in the sun, as quickly as possible.

Brewers who have sufficient space to dry their malt well enough just through air can use it to brew a clear, wine-coloured beer. Malt that is kilned on a fire kiln loses some of its strength through the heat. Making air-dried malt is impossible during the winter though, as frost can destroy the malt. During these times, the brewer needs to resort to fire to kiln the malt.

Kilning must be done slowly, first to carefully remove the moisture from the malt that can then evaporate. Quick heat closes up the barley kernel and it will stop giving off its moisture, attain an unpleasant acidity and get hard on the inside like glass.

After the malt has been dried to a hard consistency either with air or on a kiln, the rootlets need to be removed.

(Source: [10, pp. 1–10])

3.3 Friedrich Meyer (1830 & 1847)

The *Weiche*, a vessel to steep the grains, is filled with water, then the barley grains are slowly added to it. It needs to be enough water to fully cover all the barley and leave another 5 to 6 inches of space between the barley and the water surface.

Any grains swimming on the surface need to be beaten back for the first 6 to 8 hours. Grains still swimming on the surface after that time are then skimmed off. This barley is then dried and later used as animal feed, typically for pigs.

After 24 hours, the water is drained from the vessel and immediately replaced with fresh water. This is then repeated every 24 hours until the barley has been steeped sufficiently, which usually takes 3 to 4 days, as long as the water is between 7 and 12 °C.

Signs of a sufficiently steeped barley are:

- if the barley grain can be crushed between thumb and index finger from the pointy ends without it being painful.
- if the barley grain can be bent over the thumbnail without breaking, and the husks come off easily.

- if the grain, when cut in the middle, shows some moisture in the middle, without it being fully soft, dough-like or even smudgy.

While the barley is steeping, these tests need to be repeated several times. Generally, it is better that the barley is slightly under- rather than over-steeped. Under-steeping can cause some of the grains not to germinate, but this can be corrected on the malting floor by sprinkling it with water, while over-steeped barley may not provide as much extract and may attain a musty smell.

Normally, steeping the grain would last 3 to 4 hours, but there are exceptions to it. Fresh barley that hasn't completely dried out yet will steep more quickly, barley that has been steeped by traders (to increase their volume) will steep more quickly, while old, dried out barley may take even longer to fully steep.

The overall duration may also depend on other factors, such as the temperature and the cleanliness of the water. Steeping in very cold water takes longer, also steeping in soft water is quicker than steeping in hard water. With very cold, hard water under cold weather conditions and with old barley, steeping can take 5 to 6 days. Under ideal conditions though, the water temperature for steeping should be 6 to 7 °C.

Malting is not practised over the course of the whole year, but is limited to the time from September/October to April, at the most until May, to ensure that the temperatures remain low enough.

Barley of different age must not be mixed in storage, so that always barley of the same kind and of the same age is malted at once.

While steeping, the weight of the barley increases by roughly 40 to 50%, as it soaks up that much water. The steeping also extracts some of the colour from the grains, hence why the water, when drained, has a yellow colour and an unpleasant taste. Experienced brew masters claim that regularly changing the water is necessary so that the barley loses its roughness which could otherwise have an impact on the beer.

When the grain is sufficiently steeped, it is then moved to the malting floor. There, it is spread to a thickness of 3 to 4 inches so that it can dry. After 5 to 6 hours, it is then heaped up with a wooden shovel to a height of 6 to 10 inches. The surface of the heap should ideally be very even, and should have a square or rectangular footprint.

These heaps are then turned every 8 hours and this is continued until the grains start germinating and most grains show 2 to 3 rootlets. Until this time, the temperature of the barley shouldn't be considerably increased, and no "sweating" (condensation) should occur. It usually takes 2 to 3 days to reach this point.

The turning at this point happens like this: the shovel is stuck into the heap halfway, and the top half of the heap is taken off and placed next to it. Then the shovel is used to take the bottom half of the heap and put it on top of the half next to it. This places the top layer that is drier and colder underneath the bottom layer that is wetter and warmer. This turning is better done too often than not often enough as it helps even out moisture content and temperature of the grain heap.

When the grain has germinated, it is heaped up even further until it has noticeably increased in temperature and shows "sweat" on the surface. The size of the heap depends on the temperature on the malting floor. Ideally, the temperature should be 7 °C and for these temperature conditions, the heap can be about 1 foot high. With lower temperatures, the size of the heap can be increased to 15 to 18 inch. If it's warmer though, 11 to 12 °C, the heap should be lower in height and the turning shall continue for longer.

It can take 24 hours until this increase in temperature is noticeable. Under warm weather conditions, this can be as low as 15 hours, while under very cold conditions, it can also take as much as

36 hours. The ideal temperature for the heap is 17 to 20°C, but should never exceed 23°C.

Then the heap is again turned, but this time in such a way that the middle layer of the heap is spread out on the top and the bottom of the new heap, while the top and bottom layers are in the middle of the new heap. This turning is repeated when the heap has heated up again and is continued 2 to 3 times more when the grains have germinated sufficiently, in total 3 to 4 times. With every turn, the new heap should be slightly lower and wider to ensure that the temperature doesn't go up too much. At the most, the internal temperature should be at 22°C, and the heap size at the last turn should be down to 4 to 5 inches. This all in all takes about 2 to 3 days, so that the total time on the malting floor is about 5 to 6 days. Very cold temperatures can extend this by 1 to 2 days.

The barley has sufficiently grown when the rootlets are a bit longer than the grain itself, but at most 1 and 1/3 longer than the grain. Another indicator are the tips of the rootlets. When they wilt and start to turn dark yellow, then it's time to stop the germinating process. Now the barley can be called malt.

The grains are transferred to a drying floor, spread out as much as the available space allows, and turned every 5 to 6 hours. In this process, a smaller shovel is used and the malt is thrown into the air. Additionally, a brush is used before and after to get any grains that might be stuck together to come apart. If it's too cold, then the windows should be closed.

The whole point of this drying step is to stop the germinating process completely and to make the rootlets and acrospire wilt and dry off. That's why the malt should be laid out as thin as possible and turned as often as practically possible. A good airflow also helps with drying. Typically, this process takes about 2 days, but can also be finished quicker or extended even longer.

Now that the malt is sufficiently dried, it can be moved to the kiln.

The drier the malt arrives at the kiln, the better the kilning process will be, the better the malt will be and the quicker the kilning will be finished. As all of the malt can't be kilned at once, it needs to be kilned in batches. Since the remaining malt keeps on drying further, less malt shall be taken for the first batch compared to the last batch.

When the malt has been put on the kiln, the kiln is fired up and the temperature is slowly increased until it has reached a temperature of ideally 50°C, but should never go over 62°C. After 30 minutes, the malt should be turned, a process that shall be repeated every 45 to 60 minutes. The malt only gets turned between fires in kilns that are not heated by the heat of the brewery oven but are still kilned through a wood fire. When the fire has burned down, the malt is turned, then 2 or 3 pieces of wood are added to increase the fire again. Turning the malt regularly is important, but is also a task that is often done insufficiently.

Initially, a lot of moisture will be carried away, and thus, the vents need to be open fully, and should only be closed gradually later on. Only when the malt is close to be fully kilned, all vents can be closed. At this point, the malt can still be kept 1 to 3 hours on the kiln and shall be turned 2 to 3 more times. After that, it shall be removed immediately from the kiln.

Sufficiently kilned malt shows the following properties:

- the kernels are friable and easy to separate.
- when biting on the kernels, it needs to crack, like biting into freshly baked white bread.
- the inside of the kernels needs to be white as wheat flour and shall easily separate.
- a broken kernel can be used like a piece of dry chalk to make a white mark.

- rootlets and acrospires need to break off when rubbing the kernels in your hand.

Malt with these properties has been kilned correctly. It is then put into malt storage, and the next batch is kilned. By trampling the malt after taking it off the kiln but before putting it into storage, the rootlets are broken off and can later be separated more easily.

(Sources: [1, pp. 77–92] [11, pp. 109–128])

Air-Dried Malt (Luftmalz) and Wheat Malt

Air-dried barley malt is simply regular barley malt that gets fully dried on the drying floor and doesn't undergo any kilning. The author reckons that this kind of malt could also be made on kilns kept on a very low temperature. In Bavaria, it only found application in white beer brewing and the production of vinegar.

Wheat malt is also used in white beer brewing, and it is made in a similar way as barley malt. There are some differences that the brewer needs to be aware of. The steeping and the germinating process are quicker with wheat and the heaped up grains heat up more quickly compared to barley.

For malting, only winter wheat varieties are used. Steeping is done the same as with barley. The total steeping period is about 2 days, but depending on circumstances, it can also be as short as 36 hours, or as long as 3 days. water needs to be changed every 12 hours, and the steeped wheat is moved to the malting floor where it is spread out at a thickness of 3 to 4 inches.

It is turned every 6 to 8 hours, and with every turn, the size of the heap is slightly increased to an additional 2 to 3 inches in total, until the grains start germinating. This typically takes 1.5 to 2 days. It is then left until it has heated up to 19 to 21 °C. Then it gets turned, which is repeated 2 to 3 times until the grain has fully grown. With every turn, the heap is spread out slightly more.

Due to the higher amount of proteins, the rootlets need to grow longer compared to barley, to a minimum length of twice the kernel's length. Since this behaviour can differ between years and barley varieties, it is safer to instead look at the acrospire, which shouldn't quite reach the kernel's length.

If this point has been reached, the grains are moved to the drying floor and are spread out as thinly as possible. To separate the individual kernels, brushes are used, and the grains are turned every 5 to 6 hours for 1.5 to 2 days. Then the malt can be kilned. This happens at a very low temperature, less than 45 °C, and regular turning of the malt on the kiln. As soon as the malt is dry and friable enough, it is immediately removed from the kiln.

(Sources: [1, pp. 95–96] [11, pp. 132–136])

3.4 Johann Adam Messerschmitt (1836)

After the steeping vessel (*Einweichkuffe*) is filled two thirds with water, the barley is added and anything that floats on top immediately skimmed off. The water needs to sit 4 to 6 inches over the barley, not just to help with skimming, but also because the dry barley will soak up lots of water and expand in volume. The weather needs to be taken into account, as barley steeps more quickly in warm weather than in cold water. In any case, it's a good idea to change the water three times, as it helps get rid of the barley's roughness.

The exact time of steeping can't be determined, but instead, the barley needs to be checked after steeping it multiple times. The author found the right time to take the barley off the water was when he could barely bend individual grains over his thumbnail, and when cutting into a grain, the centre still had a white floury point in the middle. Such a steeped barley was supposedly more "powerful" and provided more extract than completely steeped barley. And even though barley steeped like this, combined with cold malting temperatures, takes longer to germinate, it was the author's experience that the malt produced a stronger and more effervescent beer.

When the barley is sufficiently steeped, it is moved to the malting floor in the malt cellar. This cellar should be underground and laid with stone tiles, and always be kept clean. On the malting floor, the barley is heaped up 8 inches high. It is then turned twice a day, in the morning and the evening. Before turning, it needs to be checked whether it has slightly dried in places, and if so, needs to be wetted more with well water. This is continued until the grains starts germinating.

At this point, the grains need to be turned every 8 hours. It needs to be ensured that it still is sufficiently wet so that it can continue germinating. If it is too dry in places, it needs some additional wetting. When turning, care has to be taken that the heap isn't too low or too high and that it is lower in the middle than the sides as more heat would develop in the middle of the heap.

A clear sign that indicates that the barley has sufficiently germinating is when the rootlets turn yellow. Neither a particular time nor a particular number or length of rootlets can be used to determine how long to germinate the grain. The rootlets turning yellow is the limit when the malt needs to be removed from the malting floor, otherwise the grains start growing a blade of grass which makes the malt unsuitable for brewing.

The grains are then moved from the malting floor to the drying floor. This floor needs to be covered with planks of wood. The malt needs to be spread out as thin as possible, and needs to be turned twice a day, in the morning and the evening. This turning involves throwing the malt up in the air. Throwing it up in the air upon turning, together with having a breeze of air and an open drying floor, promotes quicker drying. The drier the malt is, the better kilning will work and the "healthier" will the malt be afterwards.

The malt is kilned with a slow fire from beechwood. The malt was only ever turned when the fire was burned down. It took between 6 to 8 fires until the malt was fully dried. Properly dried malt could be recognised by the following indicators:

- a yellow colour.
- the rootlets and acrospires break off when rubbing the malt between your hands.
- a broken malt kernel can be used like chalk for writing.
- the taste of a malt kernel must be sweet.

When the malt is taken off the kiln, it is then trampled for at least 10 minutes as the rootlets and acrospires break off more easily when the malt is still warm.

Finally, the author notes that in Bamberg, no brewer used thermometers, hygrometers, or even rulers or volume measures, or took particular care of how high the malt was heaped on the kiln.

(Source: [12, pp. 44–52])

3.5 A. Herrmann (1839)

The steeping vessel is filled with water, a bit more than half full. Then the barley is added to it, with one worker using a shovel to continuously spread it out within the steeping vessel. When all the barley has been added, there should be at least one hand's width of water over it. Some barley will still swim on the water surface. It needs to be pushed down several times every 30 minutes so that any good grains will eventually sink down. When this has happened often enough, any barley still swimming on top is skimmed off and used as animal feed.

The steeping water will turn yellow or even brown and take on a particular taste. If this taste isn't removed, there is a certain danger that the grain will eventually fully steep in this unwelcome taste. This is why the water needs to be drained after about 24 hours and replenished with fresh water. It is assumed that this needs to happen at most 3 times during steeping. The final water should be totally clear when drained. In warm weather, it is necessary to drain and refill the water more often, otherwise the water can start to smell bad which would also negatively affect the grains.

How long the barley needs to steep cannot be predetermined as it depends on several factors. Steeping can take 2 days or sometimes 3 to 4 days. Generally, the following assumptions hold true, though:

- thin-husked barley takes 12 to 15 hours less to full steep.
- freshly harvested barley should be fully steeped after 36 to 48 hours.
- old or dry barley will usually take 72 hours to be fully steeped.

This is also dependent on the weather, the location and the water temperature. Soft or thin-husked barley should not steep less than 36 hours, while very dry and thick-husked barley shouldn't steep for more than 84 hours. Steeping at higher temperatures is quicker than at lower temperatures. Hard water also prolongs the required steeping time. Ideally, the water temperature should be between 7 and 12°C. Mixing old and new barley is discouraged as it will cause a very unevenly grown malt.

Sufficiently steeped barley can be recognised through the following indicators which need to be checked each with multiple grains:

- the husk easily comes off the grain and the pointy ends don't sting anymore when squeezed with two fingers.
- the grain doesn't break off anymore when bent over the thumbnail.
- one tip of the grain, near the embryo, is about to open up.

These checks ensure that the grains have been steeped properly. Generally, it is better to slightly under-steep than to over-steep, as the former only slightly delays germination, while the latter can completely destroy germinability.

When steeping is completed, the grains are brought to the malting floor where it is spread to a height of about 3 inch to dry off. It gets turned for the first time after 6 hours. This needs to be done so that any grains on the inside of the heap are then on the outside and vice versa. This is done by taking off the top half of the heap, putting it next to the heap, and then taking the bottom half and putting it on top of the new heap. This shall ensure more even drying and a more even temperature within the grain heap. This turning can be preceded by shovelling the rims of the heap towards the centre so that they will also get turned properly.

Turning the grains at this stage can hardly be done too often, but at least every 5 to 6 hours. Even drying needs to be ensured, otherwise parts of the heap could heat up too much and turn foul. Generally though, warmer temperatures require more turning than cold temperatures. In a malting floor above ground the temperatures are typically lower than in a malt cellar, which means that the malt can be heaped up more and less turning is required compared to a malt cellar.

Turning is repeated until rootlets start appearing on the grain. If the temperature is a bit warmer, turning can continue for a bit longer, but in colder temperature, the grains need to be heaped up, and is especially important when the temperature is lower than 6°C. Depending on various factors, this heap can be as low as 6 inches, or as high as 15 inches.

After this, the heap is left to rest until "sweat" is noticeable underneath the topmost layer, which usually takes 10 to 15 hours, and should be accompanied by a pleasant, fresh smell. At this point, the internal temperature of the heap should have reached 20 to 22°C, sometimes even 25°C. At least two of the rootlets should have fully formed and a third one should at least be partially there.

At this point of germination it is recommended to be especially careful that the next turning doesn't happen too early or too late. If it gets turned too early, beer brewed from the malt not only would taste less mild, it would also cause headaches and other issues, but when it's turned too late the heap could heat up too much and the grains would lose some extract.

When the heap finally gets turned, it is done according to this method: initially, the grains on the sides of the heap are removed with a shovel and put in the centre of the heap. Then the heap is turned so that the top layer ends up in the middle of the new heap, the middle layer ends up both on the bottom, the middle and the top of the new heap, and the bottom layer ends up in the middle of the new heap. The author then specifically quotes [1] (see also above) as a detailed explanation of this procedure. The first few times of turning, the middle layer can also be thrown on top, in order to form a layer that now cools off and slightly slows down germinating, while at the same time warms the layer underneath.

A less subtle method of turning is to shovel part of the heap to the side, stir it through and heap it back up. This method causes uneven malt.

When all grains have been turned, the heap is brought back into a rectangular shape so that it is even and on the side a bit higher than in the middle. In total, 4 to 5 turns are considered to be necessary.

Germination is finished when most if not all grains have 3 to 5 rootlets, each of which is about one and one third times longer than the grain itself.

Many brewers let the rootlets grow even longer as beer brewed from it clears up better and is more quickly ready for serving, but this is done at the cost of reduced extract. A brewer also shouldn't always assume the exact same length as the ideal length for the rootlets to grow, as it can vary depending on the barley that is used. Dry, thin-husked barley can be grown to just a medium length, as the protein (the original source calls it *Kleber*, lit. *glue*, which could also describe the gluten component) dissolves more easily compared to thick-husked barley that require more growth and higher temperatures for the protein to properly dissolve. Such thick-husked barley can also lead to beer that doesn't fully clarify and can also cause it to sour early.

Not turning the grains often enough is also very damaging as the inside of the heap can get too warm which can cause the grains in the centre to grow too quickly, while the outside grains will fall behind and grow too slowly. Grains that are germinating too quickly can be recognised by the acrospire being straight instead of having grown crooked or bent. During turning, the grains also must not clump together, but instead must come apart easily.

When the grains have germinated sufficiently, they're moved to the drying floor. The point of drying is to stop the germinating and prevent the grains from forming blades of grass, but also to prepare the malt for kilning by removing most of the moisture. The best place for a drying floor is a well-ventilated place near the the malting floor so that it can be easily moved over.

The drying process is not strictly necessary but has some advantages. Undried grains take longer to fully dry off on the kiln which means a higher amount of fuel that needs to be burned. Putting already (mostly) dry malt on the kiln severely reduces fuel costs.

Malt dried on a drying floor is also milder in taste, while undried malt on the kiln attains an unpleasant smell.

To carefully dry the malt, it needs to be spread out thin and turned regularly, at least every 4 to 5 hours. The drying floor needs to be large enough to support this. When turning, the malt also needs to be thrown up in the air. Initially, turning should happen more often than later on. Most malt should be sufficiently dry after 2 days. Not drying the malt quickly enough can also cause some of the grains to resume germination and to eventually form a blade of grass. Grains that have been crushed during the earlier malting process could also go mouldy.

Typically, there is more malt on the drying floor than can be kilned at once, so the malt will be kilned in multiple batches. During the kilning, the remaining malt needs to be turned.

The point of the final kilning is to remove any remaining moisture and to give the malt a hardness that makes it suitable for crushing or milling later in the brewing process. It is spread out on the kiln, at a height of 4 to 5 inches. When this is done, heat is directed underneath and the moisture of the malt evaporates. At this stage, insufficiently dried malt has a partially open husk and can take on any bad smell or taste from the heat, in particular when the malt doesn't get sufficiently turned. To achieve a good malt, it needs to be turned often on the kiln and must not get kilned too hot. Especially at the beginning of the kilning, the fire needs to be very low, the first turn needs to happen after an hour, and after that, the malt should be turned every 30 to 45 minutes.

Malt that gets dried at a higher temperature doesn't dry more quickly. Instead, the malt on the bottom gets burned easily while the malt on the top can keep some of its moisture and go bad at the high temperatures. The initial kilning temperature should be as low as 22 to 25 °C, and should only later be carefully increased to a maximum of 62 to 68 °C at which the fire is closed down and the malt shall continue kilning just from the residual heat.

During that time, it shall get turned 5 to 6 times. Malt kilned this way should be completely white on the inside, friable and dry.

Beer that is too brown from overly kilned malt always has a burnt or charred aftertaste that is enjoyed by nobody. Generally, it is an advantage for a brewer to kiln their malt to a light colour, as it not only saves fuel, but also because beer brewed from pale malt is richer and more pleasant in taste than those brewed from highly kilned malts that have lost some of their extract.

Good malt, when broken apart or bitten into, needs to crack like freshly baked bread rolls and have an inside as white as the barley itself. If the inside is yellow or brown, then the malt is bad and has lost most of its extract, even worse if it's black. A broken malt grain needs to leave behind a white mark when rubbed on something else.

Malt that is too hard to bite into is called *Steinmalz* (lit. *stone malt*), and is very bad for brewing. This fault can have several reasons, mainly because of over-kilning, but also because the inside of the grain hasn't changed sufficiently during germination, which can happen if the grain has heated up prior to malting or if it has started growing in the field already. Such malt can also happen if the grains haven't been sufficiently turned on the malting floor and have overheated, which can also happen on the drying floor or if the malt is put on the kiln in an undried state.

After sufficient kilning, the malt is brought to storage. It is poured out length-wise along the storage floor. When malt is taken for brewing, it is removed in such a way so that malt from all batches is used, which should achieve a more even colour across multiple brews. Malt should be stored for at least 2 to 3 months before it is used for brewing.

(Source: [13, pp. 22–41])

3.6 J.C. Leuchs (1839)

The author describes the situation of malting in Nuremberg. There, malting floors are built both underground and over the ground. Malting typically begins in the second half of September, and ends with the end of May.

The type of barley used for bottom-fermented beers is two-row barley. Depending on the time of year, the temperature outside and the specific properties of the barley, it is steeped for a shorter or longer time period. To determine whether it's been steeped sufficiently, it is tested by trying to break a grain over a fingernail, squeezing a grain by its pointy ends between two fingers and a general inspection of the inside of a grain. Preferably, the grain is steeped for a shorter time rather than too long. At no point shall the floury inside of the grain become a wet, white mass. Steeping usually takes 2 to 4 days, depending on the time of the year, and the water is changed once to twice a day.

When the last water has been drained, the grains are left to rest in the steeping vessel for an additional 6 to 12 hours. Barley that's being malted in autumn or spring and takes less than 2 days to be sufficiently steeped should preferably be used to brew Schenkbier rather than Lagerbier.

At the time of the year when the grains require 4 days of steeping and the water only needs to be changed once a day, it is the best for bottom-fermented beer, as the inside of the grain is only changed slowly.

After the barley has been moved from the steeping vessel to the malting floor, it gets heaped up at only 3 inches in a rectangular heap, and then turned every 6 hours. This is repeated until the first rootlet appear on the grains. Then the turning needs to be careful, in two layers, every 6 to 8 hours. At this stage, when most grains start showing a second rootlet, the grains must not "sweat" nor warm up in the heap.

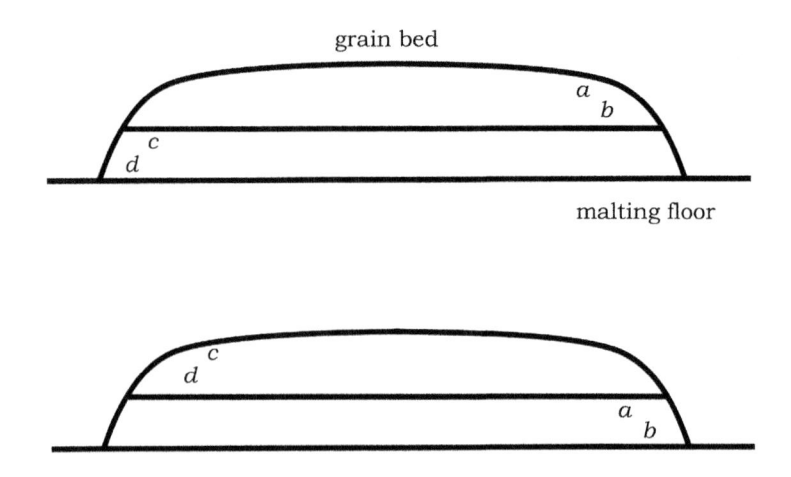

Turning malt in two layers: before (above) and after (below)

When most of the grains have achieved this state, the grains get turned again and then heaped up, ideally at a temperature of 12°C and a height of 3 inches. The outer sides should be bit higher, and the centre a bit lower. After this, it is left to rest for 12 to 15 hours. During this time, a fresh, healthy smell should appear and the grains should start "sweating". At this stage, the internal temperature of the heap should have increased to 17 to 19°C, and the first two rootlets should have fully formed and the third rootlet at half its final length.

If the heap were now turned too early, the brewed beer would end up with a less mild flavor and would cause headaches and other issues. But if it is turned too late, the rootlets would grow further than necessary and would use up some of the extract in the grain, and also heat up the whole heap of grain too much. This can also have a negative impact on the final beer.

When the heap gets turned for the first time, the resulting heap shall be 1 inch higher than the previous one. After this, it is again left alone for 8 to 10 hours, the heap should have an internal temperature of 24 to 25°C. At no point should it get warmer than this. At this stage, the rootlets start to grow more crooked, making it easier for the grains to clump up. The heap should be turned two more times before it can be spread out over the whole malting floor to cool down. It is then moved to the drying floor or directly on to the kiln.

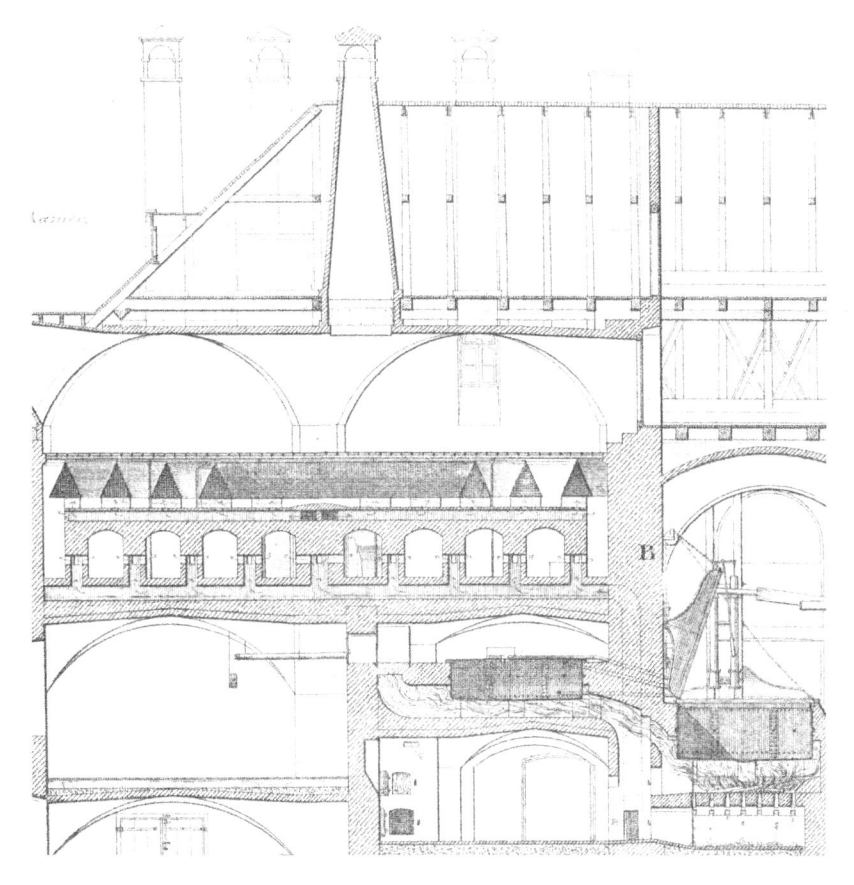

At Zacherl's brewery in Munich (nowadays Paulaner), the kettle fire (bottom right) also heated the hot-air kiln (centre left) [14]

Malt that has been grown short and only shows 4 rootlets is better suited for Lagerbier, while malt grown longer with 5 rootlets is better suited for Schenkbier. Short grown malt is also better suited for the Nuremberg brewing method: it's sufficient when the rootlets are nearly as long as the grain itself and the acrospire is about a third of the length of the rootlets. Malt with mainly 6 rootlets should better be used for top-fermented beers but is unsuitable for brewing "auf Satz" (see below). Malt with 7 rootlets should never be produced.

Air-dried malt is usable for top-fermented but not bottom-fermented beers. For this reason, malts in Bavaria are less air-dried and more kilned, though a certain amount of drying on the drying floors serves a purpose. When the malt has been sufficiently dried, it is then kilned. The most common kilns in Nuremberg at the time were so-called Dutch smoke kilns. These kilns were constructed as an inverse pyramid from which the smoke spreads through a kilning floor with holes. On the top, a vent is placed to remove the smoke and vapours. Typical firewood is beechwood.

The better breweries also have hot-air kilns where cool air is moving along heated triangle-shaped pipes. This heated air is then going through the kilning floor to dry the malt. The pipes are heated either through the brewery oven underneath the kettle, or from a dedicated small oven.

The most popular beers at the time were golden coloured ones, and thus the malt should ideally be kilned to the preference of customers. This colouration and a good quality of the malt can only be achieved when the initial kilning temperature is low, at 25°C, the malt gets regularly turned on the kiln, and the temperature at most rises to 50-62 °C. At these temperatures, the inside of the malt shall remain completely white, and the malt should eventually completely dry.

When kilning has finished, the malt gets trampled to break off rootlets and acrospires, and is then put into storage.

(Source: [15, pp. 6–13])

3.7 Leopold Limmer (1842)

The steeping vessel (*Einweichkufe*) is halfway filled with water. Then the cleaned barley is slowly added so that there are still 2 to 3 inches of water over the barley. After a few more hours, more water is added to increase this to 6 inches. The good barley will sink to the bottom, while the bad or unripe grains and any dirt, chaff, etc. will swim on top where they can be skimmed off.

It depends on the weather how long the barley needs to steep: in warmer temperatures, steeping is quicker, while with very cold weather, it can be expected that steeping takes twice the time.

The water is usually refreshed twice during steeping, but brewers in Bamberg refresh the water three times. The right time when the barley has been steeped enough can be recognised when the grains can be bent and when you cut open a grain, a small, floury point is showing up in the middle. The barley shouldn't be soaked for too long, as over-soaked barley eventually leads to stale beer. This is why, when steeping the barley, the current weather needs to be taken into account.

When the barley has steeped enough, the water is drained from vessel, and the barley is moved to the malt cellar or the malting floor. These must be cleaned beforehand and should have a stone floor. This is necessary because otherwise the barley could go bad.

On the malting floor, the barley is heaped up 8 to 9 inches high. The next day in the morning, it gets turned by lifting it all up at once. This needs to be repeated every morning and evening. After the barley has been turned a few times, it needs to be inspected whether it has dried up a bit. In this case, fresh well water shall be poured over it. It is important though to not change the temperature on the malting floor too much. If a small white yellow or white green germ appears on the barley, then the growth of the rootlets begin. From now on the barley needs to be kept a closer an eye, and needs to be turned every 10 to 12 hours. During this time, the rootlets grow which needs to be promoted by ensuring sufficient moisture (i.e. add more water if it dries out) and heaping it up higher in cold weather or lower in warm weather.

It can't be exactly determined how long it takes for the rootlets to fully form, as it depends on the age of the barley and the thickness of the husks, and not even the length of the rootlets themselves can be taken as a clear indicator. A usable indicator though is when the rootlet tips turn yellow and harden up. When this is noticeable in the whole barley heap, it gets turned one more time, spread out thin and then prepared to be moved to the drying floor. If it stayed on the malting floor for longer, then a blade of grass would start growing out of the grain, and the malt would be ruined.

The drying floor is larger than the malting floor, it is laid out with wooden planks, is airy and has been properly cleaned beforehand. The barley is spread out thin and gets turned every day in the morning and in the evening. This is apparently particularly emphasised by brewers in Bamberg. Turning the grains often not only ensures that the growth is effectively stopped, it also helps the grains to dry out evenly. This way, the grains are prepared for kilning.

If the barley was brought directly onto the kiln, the sugar in the grains would seize up and would be hard to extract. That's why it's important to dry the barley prior to kilning.

Turning the barley at this stage should be done by throwing it up into the air with a shovel. This needs to be done regularly so that the barley doesn't develop any further heat. The quicker it dries, the better will the resulting malt be. At this stage, it can't be overly dried, and brewers should take their time, at least 4 to 5 days, or even 6 days for the barley to properly dry.

Kilning happens on a low fire, and malt isn't turned until one fire has burned down. Kilning therefore takes a long time, as not a lot of malt can be kilned at the same time. Bamberg brewers typically need 6 to 8 fires. When the malt looks dry and yellow on the outside, rootlets and acrospires easily break off when rubbed between the hands, and a broken grain can be used almost like chalk to write, then the malt has been sufficiently kilned. The main care that needs to be taken during kilning is that the fire doesn't get too hot so that the malt doesn't get roasted.

Fully kilned malt then gets trampled, ideally when it is still warm so that the rootlets and acrospires fall off easily. For a typical batch size at the time, that took about 15 minutes when 2 people did it. Now the malt is ready and is stored in a dry place, ideally on a wooden floor.

(Source: [16, p. 16])

3.8 Lorenz Zierl (1843)

The steeping of the barley occurs in a vessel that is called *Quellbottich* or *Weiche*. Before the barley is added to the vessel, it is filled with water so that the barley will be fully covered with water and the water stands a few inches over the barley. Dirt and bad grains will float to the top, but are pushed down into the water every 30 minutes, for a total of 5 or 6 times, to ensure that any good kernels eventually sink down and bad ones come to the surface. After 5 to 6 hours, anything still floating on the surface is skimmed off and used as animal feed. The amount of barley that needs to be removed that way varies depending on the barley quality. Typically, it would be about 0.5 percent of the total grains by volume.

After 24 hours, the water is drained and replenished with fresh water. This needs to repeated at least 3 times, in particular during warm weather so that the barley doesn't take on any bad smell. In some breweries, the barley is not left to rest in the water, but rather some of the water is constantly drained and topped up with fresh water. If the water source is too cold, it needs to be warmed up to 10 to 11°C.

The length of steeping can't be predetermined. Freshly harvested barley that hasn't fully dried yet can be steeped within 36 to 48 hours, while older barley can take 3 to 4 days. Also the water itself and the temperature of air and water can have an influence on whether the barley steeps quicker or slower, so that sometimes, it can even take as long as 5 to 7 days.

The indicators for sufficiently steeped barley are:

- the grain can be slightly bent over the thumbnail without breaking.
- the grain can be easily pressed together on both pointy ends between thumb and index finger without it being painful; the pointy ends slightly bend over and the floury core of the grain is pushed out.
- the husk easily comes off the grain when squeezing it.
- when cut through the middle, the grain is equally wet on the inside without being doughy or smudgy.

It is better to steep too little than too much, as growing it too much can easily destroy germinability. Indicators for over-steeped grains are that when squeezing it, the inside comes out as a paste, is too pale in colour and smells bad. It's also bad if the grains are steeped unevenly as it will likely cause uneven germination on the malting floor. This often happens when barley of different age is mixed together.

When the grains are sufficiently steeped, the water is drained completely and the grains are moved to the malting floor.

There, the grains are initially spread out to a height of 5 inches, and then turned every 5 to 6 hours in such a way that the top half is put at the bottom and the bottom half is put on top of it. The idea behind this is to even out the temperature and to get evenly germinated grain. How often it needs to turned depends on several factor, such as the temperature and the amount of steeping. Generally, the temperature of the grain shall be kept low at this stage, at 10 to 15°C.

Typically, after four turns, the first signs of germination appear on the grain. At this point, all the grain is heaped up to a height of 10 to 15 inches. The specific height depends on the temperature of the malting floor: the lower the temperature, the higher the grain needs to be heaped up, and vice versa. This is described as a particular difference of Bavarian malting practice as opposed to English and Northern German malting where the malt is immediately heaped up to 15 to 18 inches right after steeping.

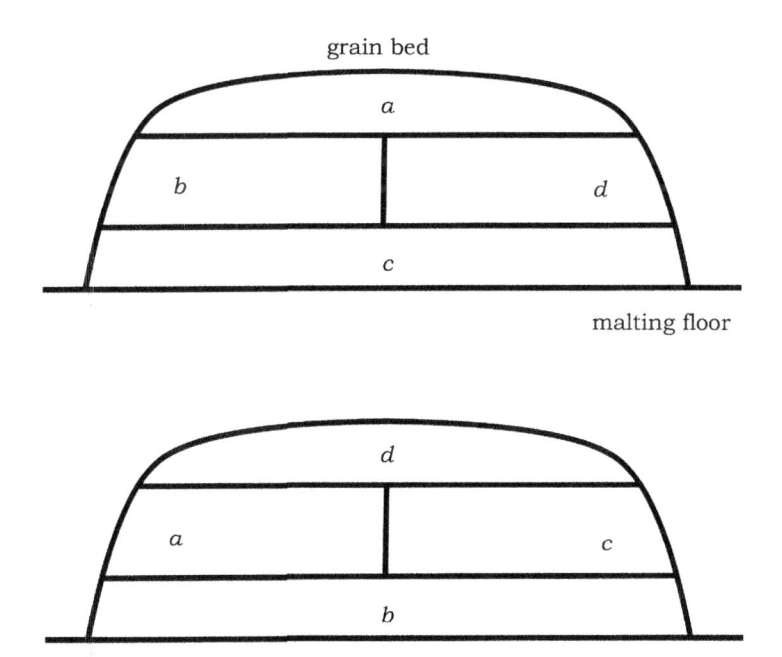

Turning malt in three layers: before (above) and after (below)

The heap is then left to rest until it has an internal temperature of 22 to 27 °C. When putting a hand in, it is also noticeable that the grain has become wet. At this point, the heap needs turning again, in such a way that the top layer ends up in the middle of the new heap, the middle layer is spread out so that some of the grains end up at the bottom of the new heap and others end up on top of the new heap, and the bottom layer should also end up in the middle of the new heap. This way, the whole heap needs to be turned 3 to 4 times. With every turn, the height of the heap is lowered, until it finally reaches just 3 to 4 inches.

The maximum internal temperature of the heap is a matter of discussion. In Scotland, it is kept close to 12 °C, and in England closer to 16 °C. Generally, 30 °C should be considered the absolute maximum.

About a day after the first rootlets have appeared, they should have grown to a length of about 0.5 inch and thus should be 1 and 1/3 to 1.5 the length of the grain itself. The treatment of the grain heap during germination is one of the most complicated bits of work in the brewery and shows the brewer's skills, as any mistakes such as the incomplete germination, over-germination or uneven germination will have a detrimental effect on the quality of the beer.

The mistake of under-germination is the rarest and only happens when the grains themselves have insufficient germinability, have been steeped insufficiently, or have been germinated at a temperature too low. More common is the mistake of over-germination that happens most often when the heap is turned not often enough or at the wrong times. The increased temperature has the worst effect on the quality of the beer, in particular if it rises to 31 to 35 °C. Sometimes brewers also make the mistake of over-germination in the hopes of being able to brew beer that clarifies more quickly. The mistake of uneven germination stems from a difference in quality of the grains themselves, uneven steeping, or other issues along the way.

Sufficiently germinated grain is then moved to the drying floor, called *Trockenboden*, *Schwelke* or *Welke*, where it is then dried to stop further germination. There, it gets turned every 4 to 5 hours, in particular when it is still slightly damp from the malting floor. If the malt remains unturned for too long, it can warm up again and resume growing or go mouldy, which would make the malt unusable for brewing. The malt shall be turned at least 6 times on the drying floor before it is put on the kiln. It should also not be kilned wet, as it would turn into badly kilned malt. If the malt on the drying floor has to be kilned in multiple batches, then the initial batch should be smaller and the last batches larger. The malt waiting to be kilned should be stirred through every 24 hours.

A kiln is constructed from a copper or iron sheet with holes in it or alternatively, a wire grid. On the ceiling, a vent is installed to remove any hot air and steam. Underneath is a dedicated room in which a fire is kept. The heated air from it goes through the holes of the metal sheets and through the malt and carries its humidity away. When malt is moved from the drying floor to the kiln, the heat is turned on. After an hour, the malt on the kiln is turned so that the malt on top is now on the bottom and vice versa. This work needs to be repeated every 30 to 45 minutes. Depending on the temperature, the malt attains different colours. The heat should never be above 62 °C, as otherwise the malt would not only develop a dark brown colour, but would also taste burnt. Most importantly, the heat must not be increased too quickly, but rather needs to be ramped up slowly. When the malt has been kilned for 9 to 10 hours, the fire is closed down but the malt is left on the kiln for another 4 to 5 hours where it is turned 4 to 5 times.

Well-kilned malt must have a white, not brown-burnt inside of a pleasant taste. When breaking a grain, it must be floury. Hard malt that looks glassy on the inside is bad and is called Steinmalz (*stone malt*). Another indicator for bad malt is an ash- or dark-grey colour.

Through the malting process, the barley has lost 8 to 10 percent in weight, but has gained 3 to 6 percent in volume, as a malt grain is larger than a barley grain. Still, a certain volume of barley does not produce the same volume in malt due to loss of the rootlets and acrospires as well as the bad grains that were skimmed off at the beginning of steeping.

(Source: [17, pp. 15–21])

3.9 Alexander Ziegler (1849)

The steeping vessel, called *Weichkasten* or *Quellkasten*, is half-filled with water, then the barley is added. Then as much water is added so that it stands 4 to 6 inches on top of the barley. This is necessary for skimming off dirt and dead kernels later.

Any grains swimming on top are pushed down. After 6 to 8 hours, anything still floating on top is skimmed off, and the water is drained and replaced with fresh water. In many breweries, steeping doesn't get the attention that it deserves, even though the author considers it a highly important step. Draining the brown and foul-smelling water early is an important step to achieve a good germinability and should happen within 24 hours as it would otherwise have a negative impact on the overall flavour of the beer later on. Ideally, draining the water and replacing it with fresh one should be repeated until it runs off clear, which is especially important in warm weather or with a higher water temperature.

With quality barley, fewer dead kernels should appear, the typical amount in Bavaria is 0.5 to 0.75 percent of the total amount by volume. Any kernels that are skimmed off are dried and then used as pig feed. The second replacement of the steeping water happens after 24 hours during winter, while in the summer, it requires a shorter amount of time. It depends on the age of the barley, the water temperature and the geometry and position of the steeping vessel how long it needs to steep.

In Munich, 2-row barley typically steeps for 72 hours with 9°C water, but the barley is left in the drained vessel for 8 to 10 hours to dry a bit before it is moved to the malting floor. Water at a temperature of 12 to 18°C is unsuitable for steeping, just as old, cold or thick-husked barley grains will take more time to steep.

One of the main rules of malting though is to use barley of the same age and the same properties for steeping to ensure even steeping and equal germination. To recognise whether the grain has steeped sufficiently, the following methods can be used:

- take a steeped grain with the pointy ends between your thumb and index finger and slowly press down on it. If pressing down on the kernel is easy and smooth while the pointy ends are slightly bending over, without any real resistance or pain on the fingers, while the husk bursts open and the inside comes out, then the grain has been steeped sufficiently.
- the husk easily comes off the grain.
- the tip of the barley kernel can be easily bent over the thumbnail.
- when putting your hand into the wet heap of barley, it feels smooth, not rough.

Proper steeping is a prerequisite to proper germination on the malting floor. Both under- and over-steeping are damaging, but the latter much more so than the former. If a squeezed kernel contains a soft mush and a certain smell, then it's been steeped for too long, germinability has suffered and the grain will be unsuitable for germination.

An over-steeped grain will germinate quickly, but the the germ will be weak and wilt quickly, the grain will contain only little sugar and would be the cause of bad beer. Under-steeped grain on the other hand will prevent the germ from breaking through the husks and in the worst case would prevent germination that way. Incomplete steeping makes it harder for the grains to germinate, but is still preferable to over-steeping because it will still lead to an even germination and can be corrected by sprinkling it with water on the malting floor.

The increase in weight and volume of the barley during steeping typically depends on the specific quality and the age of the barley. In Bavaria, it is generally assumed that steeping barley will increase its weight by 50% and its volume by 18 to 21%.

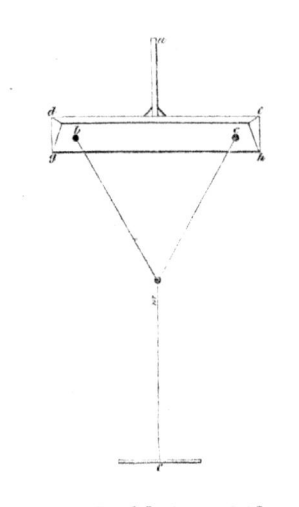

After steeping, the barley is brought to the malting floor, called *Malztenne* or *Wachstenne* (lit. *growing floor*). It is usually transported through tubes or channels from the steeping vessels onto the malting floor, where it is placed in vessels first and then shovelled into heaps which are then further spread out using a device called an *Esel* (lit. *donkey*). This device is in use by all Munich breweries.

An *Esel* [18, p. 29]

The steeped barley is then heaped up in rectangular shapes, depending on the temperature 3 to 6 inches high. These heaps initially get turned every 6 hours, later every 8 hours, and finally every 10 to 15 hours. The first turning is meant to bring the layer close to the bottom to the top and vice versa, in order to gain a more even drying of the grains and a more even germination.

The author emphasises that the temperature on the malting floor varies depending on the time of the year, and that it has an influence on how often the grains require turning and how high they need to be heaped up. During the winter, the heaps of grains closer to doors, windows, walls and pillars need to be heaped up higher. When all the grains have dried to a certain extent, the turning continues until the grains start germinating. At this point, the heap needs to be made higher, the internal temperature then increases and the grains start to "sweat". The temperature that was previously at 10 to 12 °C can now go up as high as 19 to 25 °C.

The turning process from now on needs to be done in such a way that the top layer of the old heap ends up in the middle of the new heap, the middle layer is spread out so that it ends up both on the top and the bottom of the new heap, and the bottom layer also needs to end up in the middle of the new heap.

In Munich, the heaps are usually only turned twice like this and the grains are kept in a "cold sweat" (i.e. with some moisture). The rootlets should grow evenly amongst all grains, and the whole heap should have a "good flavour", which means that it should smell like fresh, green cucumbers or apples. The turning at this stage must be done with great care so that the malt doesn't lose its moisture and keeps on germinating evenly.

The timing of all turning depends on the progress of germination and the internal temperature of the heap. Too little turning leads to uneven, unhealthy, and "suffocated" malt, while turning it too often and carelessly can disturb germination and remove too much moisture. After the first turn when germination has started, the heap must not be left unturned for too long, and in Munich is often turned within 10 to 12 hours after which it is rested for 12 to 16 hours. At the second turning, the grains must not clump up as this makes work harder and also hinders further germination.

The turned heap needs to have the same height as before and have an even surface, and the sides need to be neat and any loose grains on the side need to be brushed towards the very edge of the heap. The heap shouldn't reach an internal temperature higher than what has been mentioned before, as this is disadvantageous to the malt.

If the whole heap is "sweating" enough, additional water can be sprinkled on, but this must not be done after the second turning. It is most important that the malt doesn't germinate for too long, as it loses extract which in turn means a lower quantity of beer that can be brewed from it, even though beer brewed from malt germinated for longer would clarify more quickly. A barley grain is sufficiently germinated when it shows 2 to 4 rootlets that are about 1 and 1/3 to 1.5 times as long as the grain itself.

As soon as the barley has sufficiently germinated, this process needs to be stopped by drying it. This is done by moving the grains to a drying floor with sufficient aeration which should be located near the kiln. In Munich, a few breweries have no drying floor, whether for lack of space or because they process too much malt at once, but it's without question that this drying prior to kilning has a positive impact on the later quality of the malt and on saving fuel for kilning.

The malt is spread out on the drying floor at a thickness of 2 to 3 inches and over the course of the day is turned 6 to 7 times to prevent it from warming up. Without sufficient turning, the malt can easily continue germinating, which would make the malt unusable for brewing later on. The best times of the year for this drying process are autumn and spring because the air is usually fairly dry then. It can still be done during the winter as long as enough care is taken to prevent the grains from freezing.

When the malt is fully dried on the drying floor, it is called *Luftmalz* (lit. *air malt*). If the process of drying is finished on a kiln, it is called *Darrmalz* (lit. *kilned malt*). The point of kilning is to make the malt less perishable and to add colour as well as flavour to the beer. The colour of the beer will be darker if the malt is kilned stronger and paler if it is only lightly kilned. It can be assumed that the colour of the kilned malt rootlets will indicate the colour of the beer.

Working the kiln requires full attention of the maltster. They need to take care of regulating the heat to prevent unusable malt from being produced, from either too much heat, insufficient turning on the kiln or heaping up the malt too high on the kiln. As soon as the malt is on the kiln, a small fire is started, which is very slowly increased to effect a slow but steady increase of temperature on the kilning floor. The colour of the malt depends on the temperature. Too much heat can cause swollen, glassy and burnt malt, hence why the fire must be controlled carefully and the malt needs to be diligently and regularly turned. Hot kilns often cause a quick drying and colouration of the outer hulls of the grains without affecting the inside. This causes any expanding steam from the inside to make the malt swell up and eventually burst. When heaping up the malt too high on the kiln, combined with high heat and insufficient turning, a lot of moisture builds up and the malt "drowns in its sweat". Glassy and burnt malt will later also be hard to dissolve during mashing, will add a burnt, rough taste and a red-brown, "foxy" colour to the beer.

Depending on the size of the kiln, the malt is spread out thicker or thinner. It needs to be turned every 45 to 60 minutes. This always needs to be done in such a way that all malt is turned and remains at the same overall thickness of how it is spread out. The heat of the kiln should not go over 65°C as this would cause many of the issues mentioned before. As soon as all the moisture has been driven off, the fire and all the vents are closed to keep the heat in. After 10 to 12 hours, the kilning of the malt is finished. This can be recognised by the malt being easy to bite open or break up, that it contains white flour on the inside and tastes slightly sweet, similar to sugar. Other signs of good quality malt include a thin husk and a plump, heavy kernel.

The author notes that the manufacturing of *Farbmalz* (lit. *colour malt*, i.e. black malt) as well as colouring beer with caramelised sugar is uncommon in Munich, even though both techniques have the advantage of having greater control over the colour of beer while saving costs and work.

When the malt has been kilned sufficiently, the rootlets and acrospires are trampled off which still takes place on the kilning floor. Then the malt is moved to storage where it gets cleaned and stored for later use in brewing. The broken off rootlets can be used as fertiliser or as animal feed.

The weight of the barley is reduced through malting, while the volume is increased. 100 Pfund of barley, after kilning and cleaning and subtracting 10% water loss, make about 91 to 93 Pfund of barley malt. 100 Scheffel of barley will produce 100 to 103 Scheffel of malt that has been freed from its rootlets and cleaned.

(Source: [18, pp. 26–49])

3.10 P. Müller (1854)

The purpose of steeping is to soften the husk and the endosperm, so that it contains enough moisture to start germination. For that, the steeping vessel (*Weiche* or *Gerstenbütte*) is filled half-way with water, then the barley is added and thoroughly stirred through. If there is not enough water in the vessel so that it stands 6 to 8 inches over the barley, more needs to be added and stirred again.

The good barley will sink to the bottom, while the light and dead kernels as well as other dirt will swim on top. After 5 to 6 hours, it gets stirred again so that any remaining good grains will eventually sink down so that everything else floating on top can be skimmed off.

After the water has washed off plenty of dust from the barley, but also started extracting a yellow matter called *Loh* (a German word otherwise associated with tanning) from the grains, it should be drained at this point and replaced with fresh water.

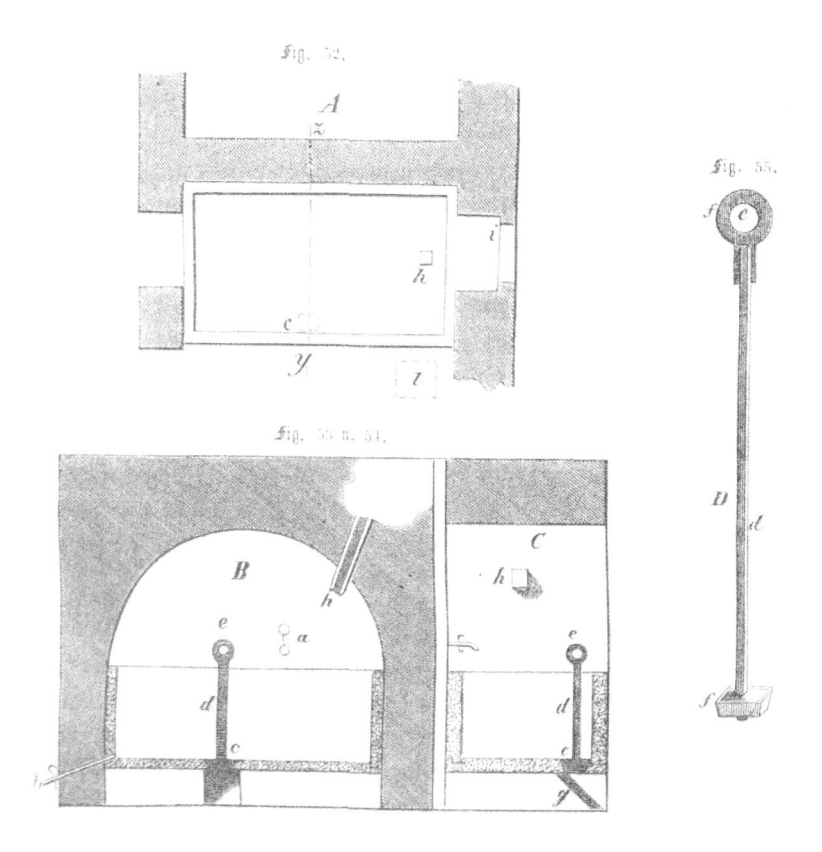

Construction of a *Weiche* [19, p. 149]

Initially, the grains will take on the most water, so it needs to be ensured that they will always be covered with enough water. During the winter, it is sufficient to renew it after 24 hours, but in spring and late autumn, or generally during warm weather, this should be done every 12 hours, otherwise the water may turn foul, badly smelling or even acidic which would have a negative impact on the barley and the malt later on.

If you notice a shimmering layer on the water, it needs to be taken off before the water is renewed, otherwise it attaches itself to the grain and can cause it to go mouldy.

The amount of time to steep the barley depends on the time of the year, the barley's age, the husk thickness, the quality of the water, the steeping vessels, the location and the temperature. But generally it can be assumed that in late autumn, when the barley is still fresh and hasn't completely dried, steeping should be done within 36 to 48 hours, while in the winter, assuming it's not too cold, it can easily take 3 full days (3 times 24 hours). During spring, when the weather gets warmer again, 6 to 12 hours less time are required.

But if the barley is very dry and has thick husks, it can take up to 4 days, sometimes even half a day longer, to fully steep it during winter.

At this point it should very clear that the barley used should all be of the same quality. Old barley shouldn't be mixed with young one, thick-husked not with thin-husked, not even barley that has grown of different types of soil. All these factors could easily cause very uneven steeping.

Soft water also effects a quicker steep than hard water. Since the temperature of the water should not increase over 15 °C, steeping vessels made from stone plates should be preferred as it should keep the steeping water cooler compared to wooden steeping vessels. Stone vessels are also easier to clean.

The length of steeping also matters, as under-steeped grains can dry more quickly later on, which could cause issues with germination. Are the grains over-steeped so that the inside is milky, then it is much worse and the grains won't evenly germinate, as other destructive processes besides germination are going on inside the kernel.

Sufficiently steeped barley can be recognised like this:

- when the husk easily comes off the grain and looks like about to break up where the rootlets are meant to appear.
- when the steeped grain can be bent over the thumbnail without breaking off.
- when the pointy ends of the steeped grain aren't stingy anymore.
- when a grain from the middle of the steeping vessel can be slightly squeezed between thumb and index finger without much resistance, the grainy flour on the inside can be felt and the husk breaks up length-wise.

It's not enough to just test a single grain, but rather a number of grains across the steeping vessel.

When the barley is sufficiently steeped, the water is drained and the barley is left in the vessel for a few hours, then it is moved to the malt cellar or malting floor.

Balling argued that the conventional method of steeping had some disadvantages, in particular that it extracted too much from the grain during prolonged steeping. He had also noticed that such grains, when planted in soil, would actually not grow particularly well, instead ending up with a weak plant. Balling instead suggested another method, where the grain was initially steeped as normal, but with only 18 to 24 hours of direct contact with water in total, during which the water is drained and replaced twice. After that, the grains are moved to the malting floor where they are heaped up about a foot high in a rectangular shape. After an hour, the whole heap is sprinkled with water from a watering can under continuous turning. As soon as this water has been soaked in by the grains, the sprinkling and turning is continued until all grains have taken on enough water. The regular turning assures that the grains are all evenly steeped. With this method, the endosperm is not being touched by the moisture which does not negatively affect germinability.

As with the conventional method, the barley still needs to be tested in the same way as before whether it has been sufficiently steeped. The remaining method of malting remains the same.

Another method that has originated in England but has recently found use in Munich is the use of a *Nachweiche* or *couch*, a separate vessel in which the grains are kept for 10 to 15 hours after steeping before they are being transferred onto the malting floor. If the grains are kept in it for longer than 15 hours, they need to be turned, otherwise they would heat up too much.

A third method was the Bohemian method as it was applied in Prague, where the grain was steeped for 24 hours, then the water was drained and the grain was moved the malting floor where it was heaped up to a cone of 4 to 5 foot and then sprinkled with water every 30 minutes and turned. After the 22 to 23 hours, this heap is moved back into the steeping vessel, where it remains for another 6 to 8 hours until it has been sufficiently steeped. It is then moved to the malting floor.

When it comes to germination, different breweries prefer different methods. Some breweries use a method that is called "malting in cold sweat" that achieves a malt with rather short-grown rootlets, while others prefer a higher temperature during germination which causes the grains to grow rootlets of a length of 1 3/4 to 2 times the length of the grain itself. While this has the advantage of forming more diastatic power, it also brings great disadvantages with it. For this reason, the author thinks that growing grains to a medium length is a good compromise.

After the grain has been steeped the conventional way, it is moved to the malting floor where it is spread out thin to a height of 3 to 5 inches. It is first turned after 4 to 6 hours and then, depending on the time of the year and the temperature of the malting floor, heaped up to a square heap of 6 to 10 inches height. Ideally, this heap should be kept away from the walls as far as possible as they have a different temperature than the rest of the floor. It is necessary to regularly turn the barley while it is still wet so that the individual grains dry evenly so that they can then grow better.

At temperatures of 10 to 12 °C on the malting floor, the heap gets turned every 12 hours, while with higher temperatures, it needs to be turned every 6 to 8 hours. Every turn preserves the height of the heap. After 30 to 40 hours, it should warm up internally, and the development of the rootlets begins.

At this point, a light "sweating" should be noticeable underneath the top layer of barley, and the grains should show white dots where the rootlets are on the way of getting out. The heap is then turned again while its height is slightly reduced, and then the maltster waits until the internal temperature has increased to 17 to 22 °C, while the first rootlets appear and slowly grow.

If the malting cellar is below 10 °C, or if the malting floor is above the ground during the cold weather, malting is very difficult and should rather not be practised. If malting can't be avoided, the heap can be made higher by 1 to 2 inches, or the malting floor could also have slight heating put on, to ensure that the germinating grains start "sweating" and the growth is not interrupted too much due to the low temperatures.

Under these circumstances it is also not advisable to throw the grains up too much in the air, as it would cool down the heap too much and it would be much harder for it to regain the right internal temperature.

During warm weather, twice the care is necessary, and not only should the height of the heap be decreased to just 6 inches, it should also be turned more often to help cool it down. As soon as it has reached a temperature of 17 to 22 °C, it gets turned again. After it has again reached this temperature, the grains should show 3 to 4 rootlets by now which should have grown longer and be intertwined with each other. The heap then again requires turning, but the resulting heap needs to be slightly lower in height than before.

This way, the heap needs to be turned a total of four times, reducing the overall height every time, until the barley has sufficiently germinated at which point it gets thrown apart to cool down before it is moved to the drying floor.

The author recommends to put the uttermost care and diligence into this process if you want to achieve an evenly grown, state-of-the-art malt. It is especially important to ensure that the internal temperature of the grain heap never goes over 22 °C as otherwise the rootlets would grow very unevenly and longer than necessary. It also needs to be avoided that the grains clump together too much by their rootlets.

With this malting method, the rootlets should be about 1 and 1/3 as long as the grain itself, and the grain should have 3 to 5 rootlets which should look crooked, i.e. should not have grown straight as this would be a sign that they have grown too quickly and thus unevenly.

If you grow the rootlets longer than this, then you will get a beer that clarifies more quickly but will also be less nutritious, while growing the rootlets shorter than this, the beer won't clarify as easily and won't be quite as strong, either.

One of the visual indicators that can be noticed on the germinated grains is the endosperm and how it has progressed in its growth. Unless growth is stopped at the right time, it will appear opposite of the rootlets as a blade of grass and is called *Säbel* (lit. *sabre*) or *Husarensäbel* (lit. *husar's sabre*) in German brewing jargon. Letting a blade of grass appear is a big error as every brewer should know.

As it can be safely assumed that enough diastatic power has formed and part of the starch has dissolved only when the endosperm has grown to a length of about 3/4 of the grain, its growth needs to be stopped together with the growth of the rootlets.

Letting the endosperm grow longer or even break out of the grain would mean a loss of useful substance, as the growth requires nutrition, and the malt in turn would lack that amount and would produce wort with less extract and thus a weaker beer.

An exact observation of the endosperm is therefore equally important, and for anyone who is not aware of that yet, it shall be noted that a grain and its endosperm can be inspected better when the husk is removed with a penknife.

As for the turning itself, it is important to do this in such a way that any grains that have previously been on the bottom and top end up in the middle of the new heap, while the grains in the middle end up on the top and the bottom. This is done to ensure an equal contact with air, but also a more even temperature.

As soon as rootlets start appearing, the grains need to be turned more carefully, according to this process: the outer layer of the heap is taken off and without turning, thrown into the middle, i.e. the complete surface of the heap. This is also done with the top half inch of the cold layer on top that is thrown on top of the heap the same way.

Now a part of the warmer inside is picked up with shovel, turned and spread out beside you on the floor. The same happens with the second part, but it is spread a bit more, finished by the third part which is again thrown to end up more in the middle. This is continued for the rest of the heap all the way to the end of the malting floor.

Then the sides of the heap are shoveled up so that they are slightly higher than the middle of the heap. That way, it can develop roughly the same temperature in all spots and thus germinates at the same speed. Finally, the surface of the whole needs to be flattened and be all at the same height to ensure an equal temperature across the whole heap and thus an equal germination of all grains.

If it still happens that the grains germinate unevenly, then this is usually because of the specific floor of the malting cellar or different temperatures from adjacent rooms that hinder even germination. In this case it's the maltster's responsibility to even this out by slightly changing the height of parts of the heap.

Another rule to make good malt is to avoid crushing any grains on the malting floor. Crushing grains stops their germination, the grain dies off and goes bad. As it is amongst other growing kernels, it also provides nutrition to them, again causing an uneven growth. More crushed grains mean a greater disadvantage of more unevenly germinated grains. The damage is double here: on the one hand, a number of grains are lost, while others are over-germinated, both of which reduce the overall amount of usable substance to achieve a rich wort. It is therefore recommended to walk on the malting floor with felt shoes only.

Malting wheat is generally done the same way as barley. It only requires a shorter steeping time and more care due to quicker germination. Steeped wheat is heaped up lower, requires turning often so that the temperature never exceeds 15 °C, and when at most 3 rootlets have appeared, they should not be longer than the grain itself. At this point, further germination needs to be stopped by cooling the grains by throwing them apart.

If a wheat kernel only shows a single rootlet, it is a sign that is has been over-steeped. When germinating evenly, the endosperm should only move a tiny bit. Whenever the rootlets have reached their proper length, it will start growing more quickly and turn yellow-green. This needs to be avoided by throwing the grain apart. When 6 to 8 grains have clumped together by their rootlets, it is time to move the malt to the drying floor and get it to dry as quickly as possible by thorough turning.

When the malting in general is done with skill and great attention, then only very few kernels should be in it that haven't germinated. Also here the age and the quality of the barley have an influence, as the overall quality varies year by year. Experience shows that in some years, barely one out of 1000 grains doesn't germinate, while in others, as many as 10% fail to germinate properly.

The best time for malting is spring and autumn when the temperatures are moderate. During the winter, the malt cannot dry properly on the drying floor, while during the summer, the temperatures are too high and the grain will germinate very quickly and unevenly, unless the malting floor is in a very cool cellar and the steeping vessel is also located there.

Generally speaking, the slower and more evenly the germination process is conducted, the better will be the quality of the malt. Keeping the temperatures low can never cause any damage, while high temperatures cause the endosperm to grow quickly, or when it's even higher, it can cause the rootlets to wilt and fall off, thus stopping the germination process early.

It needs to be repeated again that the good progress of malting can be noticed best in the continuous, slow growth of the rootlets, and also that the heap of grain starts to smell pleasantly like apples. If the opposite happens, then the grains have not been turned sufficiently, the temperature has increased considerably and through the type of fermentation that has been started that forms acidity and foulness, the malt has been robbed of the ability to produce a strong and durable beer.

When the malt is sufficiently germinated, it is moved to the drying floor, where the rootlets will wilt and fall off, but also where the whole kernel can dry before it is kilned. To achieve this, the malt is spread out thin and turned at least 2 to 3 times a day (the more often the better) with a shovel by throwing it in the air. This is necessary to completely stop germination. The thinner it lies on the floor, the more it is turned, the quicker it will dry, and the better the following kilning will go. The drying process also means a considerable saving in fuel for kilning.

In places where white beer is brewed, *Luftmalz* is used, which is just fully dried malt from the drying floor. But even for these malts, it is better to put these on a kiln at a very low temperature to ensure even further drying, which also makes it easier to remove the rootlets, which has a positive impact on the beer quality. As with the malting floor, crushing the malt on the drying floor should also be avoided, as crushed grains tend to go mouldy.

Kilning is done for two purposes:

- to completely dry off the rootlets and to get the malt in such a dry state that it can be stored and later milled for brewing.
- to give it colour and a slight flavour of burnt sugar by slightly roasting it, but mostly to be able to use it to brew a durable beer that doesn't tend to go sour easily.

The air-dried malt is spread evenly on the kiln in a layer of 5 to 6 inches. The fire needs to be put on very low, and the malt needs to be initially turned every 15 minutes, later every 30 minutes. Depending on how fully dried the malt has been before kilning, the temperature needs to be adjusted accordingly. Too much heat when the malt is still slightly damp would cause the malt to harden up quickly and go brown, while the drying on the inside cannot happen properly anymore and would cause the kernel to pop open from the heat.

If undried malt is put on the kiln, then even more care is required and a low temperature needs to be kept, as a high temperature would otherwise cook the inside of the kernel and form a gelatinised mass that would be hard like horn after drying. Malt in this condition is unusable for the brewing process as the hot water is unable to access the extract. Spent grains would contain such malt essentially unchanged even after the complete brewing process.

Even if this doesn't happen, too much heat can cause a very hard malt (*Glasmalz*, lit. *glass malt*) to form, which is also practically impossible to mash in.

Therefore it is imperative that the malt can only be heated up slowly and gradually.

The malt on the kiln needs to be turned diligently, and any steam or fumes coming from the malt need to be extracted through a vent, otherwise it could re-condense and not only leave behind a rather unpleasant taste but also make the kilning harder.

If the turning doesn't happen frequently enough, the result can be a burnt malt (*Steinmalz*, lit. *stone malt*). This malt contains a black, coarse flour that provides no extract.

A slow fire with a gradually increasing heat of a maximum of 62, at most 75 °C is a main condition for kilning good malt. Too much heat not only reduces the diastatic power, but can ultimately even completely destroy it.

For kilning wheat malt, it needs to be completely air-dried beforehand. If it was kilned wet, it would shrink even at temperatures as low as 56 °C.

While malt on the kiln in general really would only need as much temperature as is absolutely necessary to completely dry it out, the temperature of up to 75 °C also helps slightly roast it. If a brewer brews for customers who are used to dark beer, it is recommended though that the brewer shouldn't roast their whole malt to the desired colour, but rather to produce a small quantity of dark roasted malt (so-called *Farbmalz*, lit. *colour malt*) that is added to the regular brewing malt during milling.

When using smoke kilns, only fully dry beechwood should be used as fuel, while air kilns (kilns that work with heated air, also called *Rohrdarren*, lit. *pipe kilns*) can use any kind of fuel, like hard coal or peat.

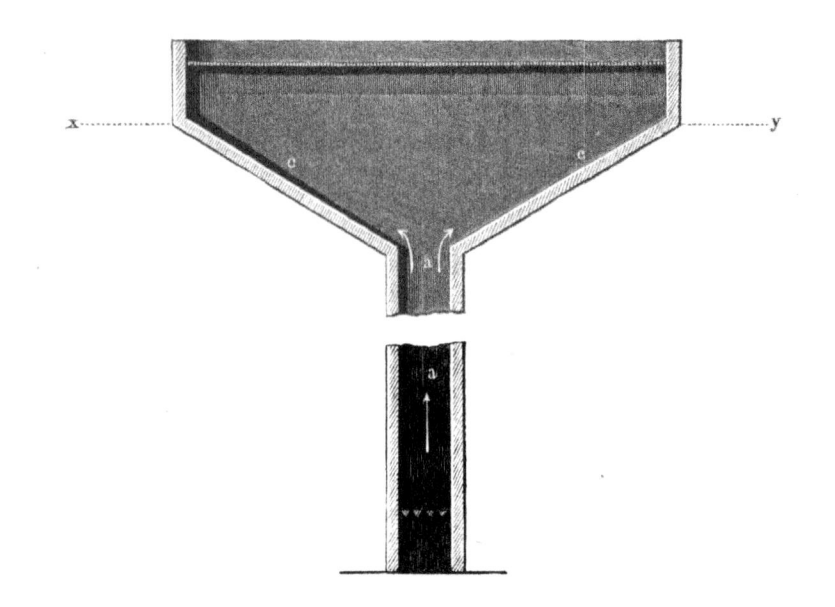

A simple construction of a smoke kiln [20]

Beer made from kilned malt is less perishable than those made from air-dried malt, and it has, depending on the degree of kilning, a darker colour and a nicer taste. It also clarifies more easily, but will not attenuate as well as beer from air-dried malt.

When the malt is finished kilning, it is moved to a wooden floor where it is spread out and, while it's still warm, is trampled with wooden shoes in order to get the rootlets to break off. When this is done, the malt is left for another 8 to 10 hours to fully cool down.

(Source: [3, pp. 145–172])

3.11 Philipp Heiß (1860)

The steeping vessel (called *Weiche* or *Quellkasten*) is made from wood, stone or cement. It is filled with water in such an amount that it will cover the barley by a few inches. Then the barley is slowly added to the water so that any dust or dead kernels remain on the water surface. Then the barley is evened out. After an hour, any barley still floating on top is skimmed off and used as animal feed.

The time of steeping depends on several factors:

- the age of the barley, whether it's one year old or even older than that.
- whether the water is more or less rich in minerals, i.e. whether it is hard or soft.
- the time of the year, i.e. the outside temperatures, also the water temperature, especially when water from a reservoir instead of a well is used.
- the location of the steeping vessel, and where it is cold or tempered.

The typical steeping time is 40 to 48 hours in spring and autumn, and 3 to 5 days in winter.

Common Steeping Method

After the initial steps as described above have been done, the old water is drained after 12 hours and replaced with fresh water. In spring and autumn this needs to happen twice so that the water in the steeping vessel doesn't warm up too much and starts to smell bad, which would be a great disadvantage for the beer. The water and the location of the steeping vessel should therefore always have a temperature between 10 and 15 °C. The first water that is drained contains a lot of extracted substances from the barley, is of a yellow colour, has a bitter taste, smells like straw water and – when stirred – foams up like beer.

It must also be noted that if a shimmering layer forms on the water, it needs to be skimmed off before draining the water, otherwise it attaches itself to the grains which can then easily get mouldy.

Steeping According To Chemical Considerations

The barley is cleaned of any dead kernels, chaff and dust by letting it into the water as described above. After about 18 to 24 hours the water is drained off and the barley is moved to the malting floor where it is spread out so far that it is heaped up 6 to 8 inches high. Then this heap is sprinkled with fresh water from a watering can and diligently turned. This is repeated every 30 minutes until the grains are sufficiently steeped. The regular turning will lead to a more even steeping.

English Steeping Method

Another even more practical method exists that fulfils the same purpose in England and at the time of writing also in the new brew-house of Mr. Sedlmayr (of Spaten brewery) by using a *Nachweiche* (lit. *post-steeping vessel*, English term *couch*). After the barley has been almost completely steeped, it is moved to this separate vessel in which it remains for another 10 to 15 hours, depending on the temperature on the malting floor.

If the barley has been in the *couch* for longer than 15 hours, it needs to be turned, otherwise it would warm up too much.

The effect of the last two steeping methods is the following: first, a more even steeping process; second, less extraction from the grain during steeping as the contact with water is shorter than with the common method. In particular changing the water keeps on dissolving more parts of the grain, which not only lowers the overall extract that can be achieved, it also reduces the overall diastatic power of the barley.

Sufficiently steeped grain can be recognised by the following indicators:

1. the husk comes off easily from the grain.
2. the husk seems to break open where the rootlet is about to come out.
3. the husk immediately bursts open when the grain is squeezed length-wise between thumb and index finger without it being painful.
4. the grain can be bent over a thumbnail without breaking.
5. when trying to bite on it, it doesn't spread out wide.
6. when drawn over a board, the grain leaves behind a chalk-like mark.

When the barley has been sufficiently steeped, it is moved to the malting floor. There, it is spread using a wooden device called *Esel* (lit. *donkey*). When this is done, turning the grains with a shovel begins. The time of this varies and depends on the malting floor's temperature. The best room temperature would be 10 to 15 °C, at which the heap of grain should be 6 to 10 inches thick and get turned every 8 to 10 hours. This is assumed as an average temperature, and depending on whether the temperature increases or decreases, the time of turning also changes, in particular, the warmer it is the more often, and the colder it is the less often the grain needs turning. The turning is done to keep the heap of grain at a constant temperature of 15 to 20 °C so that all grains start germinating at the same time. Unturned, the heap surface would dry out. Therefore, it needs to be put on the bottom and the bottom layer needs to be put on top with every turn, which not only evens out the temperature but also ensures more even drying and germination.

The author then formulates a number of practical rules for turning the grains at this stage:

1. the heap should be as far removed from the walls as possible, i.e. it shouldn't touch any of them.

2. before turning, the maltster should remove the outer layer of the heap and throw it towards the middle of the heap, because the outside is colder than the rest of the heap and would otherwise stay behind in germination.
3. the heap needs to be turned in two steps so that the top half ends up on the bottom and the bottom half ends up on top of the new heap.
4. the maltster should work away from the floor and keep clean paths, i.e. no grains shall remain on the bottom that have previously been on the bottom; they also shouldn't step on the heap, as the wet and soft grains could get crushed easily and thus be lost for brewing.
5. the heap should also be flat on top, in particular in such a way that there are no high or low points, otherwise germination would be uneven. If the specific conditions don't allow for even germination of a flat heap, the height needs to be adjusted to be higher where germination is slower and lower where germination is faster.
6. the sides of the heap need to be slightly higher than the centre of it.

When germination has progressed so far that virtually all grains have rootlets that are about 1/3 of the length of the grain, the heap is made slightly higher, and the turning method is changed to turn in three layers. The exact times for when to heap up and when to turn for the first time are some of the most crucial moments during malting. Neither of them shall be done too early or too late. On the first turn, the whole heap needs to have a good, fruit-like smell and shall be humid enough. If it is turned without that necessary humidity, it would dry out too quickly.

The exact time when a heap needs to be turned can't be exactly determined, as it depends on its internal temperature. It is imperative to use a thermometer at this stage and to always keep in mind that the germination of barley shall be done at the lowest temperatures possible. According to the author, many other books talk about an ideal temperature of 22 to 30 °C, but experience has shown that when germination has progressed sufficiently, the internal temperature of the heap shall never be more than 15 to 20 °C.

If the grain is allowed to warm up too much and and not turned often enough, it will eventually develop a sour fermentation and eventually go bad, which is noticeable through a foul smell. It shall therefore be assumed that when the heap exceeds a temperature of 15 to 20 °C, it shall be turned and after turning shall have an internal temperature of 12 to 15 °C. This temperature, if it isn't already naturally present at the time of the year, shall be kept artificially this way. For this, the malting floor should be situated so that it never gets too warm or too cold, ideally below the ground. Malting floors on the ground floor for this reason are really only usable during spring and autumn.

On a malting floor with even temperatures, assuming that the ideal internal temperatures aren't exceeded, the barley should be finished germinating after 4 to 5 days. On ground floor malting floors though, this can take 8 to 10 days during cold weather, even when the malting floor is heated. Despite that, you barely get good malt because the floor itself remains very cold and sufficient germination can only be achieved by heaping it up very high.

Again, the author formulates several practical rules for turning the grains after they've shown rootlets:

1. the maltster needs to know how to use a shovel; turning a heap requires a lot of attention and practice.
2. the heap shall be generally a bit higher than during the initial phase of germination. After every turn, it needs to be spread out slightly thinner so that after the last turn, it is spread out over the whole malting floor.
3. before the barley is moved to the drying floor, it needs to be turned in such a way that the grains are only slightly clumped together.

4. if the grains germinate unevenly, this needs to be counteracted by heaping the grains up thicker or thinner. If this isn't enough or the difference is substantial, then the heap may require dividing. This is especially necessary with 2 year old barley.
5. if the barley has been removed from steeping too early, it should have been sprinkled with water during the early stage of germination; if this hasn't happened sufficiently and the heap doesn't start developing an internal moisture at the later stages of germination, it also requires sprinkling with water.
6. the heap must never remain unturned for too long or it would heat up too much.

Indicators of well-germinated malt:

1. the grain, when bitten into, should appear white and floury.
2. the endosperm can be easily squeezed out of the husk between the fingers and rubbed into flour.
3. the rootlets should be thick and look crooked; their length should be about 4/3 of the grain and 3 to 4 of them should be noticeable on every grain.
4. the acrospire under the husk should be at least 2/3 the length of the grain.

The opinion of brewers about the length of rootlets and acrospire are divided; most let grains germinate too long, usually for the reason that such malt produces beer that clarifies better and runs off better from the spent grains. The reason for turbidity can be entirely different, though:

1. if the heap has been kept too warm on the malting floor.
2. if the mill stones have heated up the malt too much during milling.
3. if the crushed malt has heated up too much during warm weather.
4. if the first heat in the mash tun is too high.

5. if the malt is still slightly humid from the drying floor and gets kilned with too great a heat.

It should be obvious to an experienced brewer that a stronger beer takes longer until fermentation is finished and thus will clarify later compared to a weaker beer made from over-germinated malt that has lost some of its extract.

To interrupt germination and to stop any further growing, the malt is brought to the drying floor. These should have a good draught from all sides, and the malt should be spread out as thin as possible so that all the grains are touched by the air and can be sufficiently cooled and dried to interrupt germination. This is the main purpose of the drying step, and it can only happen by removing the two factors that have previously driven it, i.e. humidity and warm temperature. For that, the malt also needs to be turned regularly, about every 4 to 6 hours, especially so during warm weather. The more moisture the malt loses at this step, the better, as it means that less time and fuel would be required on the kiln.

The author then lists a few rules for drying:

1. the drying floors need to be large and well-aired.
2. the malt needs to be spread out as thinly as possible.
3. the malt needs to be regularly turned so that it doesn't get warm or mouldy.
4. the malt needs to be thrown high up in the air during turning to help with drying.

The next step after drying is kilning. As with drying, one of the most important pre-conditions for a good kiln is good ventilation that removes any humidity as quickly as possible. Kilning the malt is necessary to produce a durable beer that doesn't go sour easily and is done by warming up very thin layers of malt up to a certain temperature. This causes any further humidity to evaporate, the malt to dry completely, and to dry off the rootlets.

Two types of kilns that were common at the time were single kilns and double kilns. According to the author, double kilns are strongly preferable. Such a kiln is constructed with two kilning floors, a lower and an upper one. On the upper floor, the malt can dry first, and when the malt on the lower floor is fully kilned, it is removed from there, and the half-dried malt from the upper floor can be transferred to the lower floor. This drastically speeds up the kilning process and prevents bad kilned malt from being produced.

Malt can either be put on the kiln directly from the malting floor (where it is called *Grünmalz*, lit. *green malt*) or from the drying floor. The latter case saves kilning time and fuel. The resulting malt is also milder than malt made from *Grünmalz*. The kilning process with *Grünmalz* also needs to be much more careful when it comes to the removal of moisture. Good kilned malt can be mashed in easily, unlike *Grünmalz* which is hard to mash in and also saccharifies incompletely in the mash. This means that kilning causes a change in the malt that has a positive impact on the mashing process.

Kilning methods can also be distinguished by how hot air is applied to remove moisture. One method is the use of smoke, the other method is the use of hot air. Smoke kilns (*Rauchdarren*) are constructed in such a way that the smoke together with hot air permeates the malt directly and drives off any moisture as steam.

The smoke leaves behind a particular flavour in the malt which is easy to taste. Another big disadvantage of smoke kilns is that it requires well-dried beechwood as fuel, as other fuel would make the beer undrinkable. This is the reason why smoke kilns have fallen out of fashion and are mostly to be found in smaller country-side breweries.

Hot-air kilns (*Luftdarren*) on the other hand work on the principle that a system of tubes heats up the surrounding air which is then used to dry the malt.

Green malt [21]

The temperature at which the malt is kilned has a large influence on the later quality and properties of the malt and thus on the resulting beer. As long as there is some humidity within the grain, a part of the starch is turned into sugar through the diastase (amylase enzymes), which is the reason why air-dried malt contains more starch than kilned malt, while kilned malt tastes sweeter than air-dried malt, making the resulting beer milder than air-dried malt, which causes beer to have a rough taste.

These changes in the malt can only be explained by the increased temperatures during kilning. Additionally, it needs to be noted the kilning temperature also has an influence on the malt colour and thus also the beer colour, which needs to be considered with regards to customer preferences. If malt gets kilned at 87 to 100 °C, it turns quite dark, sometimes even black and smells like roasted coffee. This malt is called *Farbmalz* (lit. *colour malt*) which can be used in small quantity to give the wort the preferred colour. It is used especially often together with air-dried malt, where 1/4 Pfund per 100 Pfund of wort are enough to give it a nice colour.

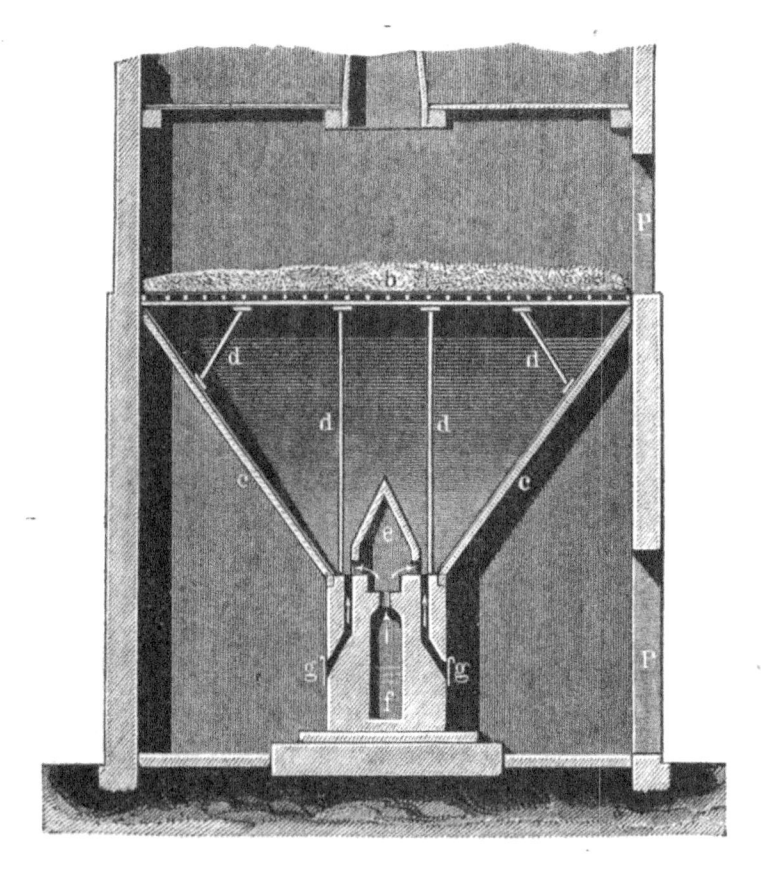

A more advanced type of smoke kiln [20]

Every practical beer brewer will have to concede that it is easier to work with dark malt and thus a darker beer colour than with pale ones. Any mistakes are much easier to recognise with pale malts and beers as they are more sensitive compared to dark ones, and a dark beer made from the same amount of malt will taste stronger and sweeter than a pale beer. The darker a malt is kilned, the more heat is required, and thus, the more sugar will be burnt in it. This burnt sugar dissolves during mashing but isn't turned into ethanol during fermentation, but instead remains as dissolved sugar in the beer, which is where the strength and the sweetness of dark beer is coming from.

Dark beers therefore are easier for the brewer when it comes to consumer preferences, not just because of the easier work, but also because more dark and pale beer can be brewed from the same amount of malt.

(Source: [22, pp. 28–66])

English Method

In England, even though maltings are set up in a very simple fashion, excellent malt is produced. Malting is strictly separated from brewing there and forms a separate line of business. Malt factories are constructed in such a way that on one end, there's the steeping vessel, and on the other end there's the kiln. In between are 4 to 5 fields (malting floors) beside and on top of each other, each of which is large enough to contain the full amount of barley of one batch to be malted.

The operation of the malting process itself is done in such a way that the different fields contain barley at different stages of germination, and in such a way that the fields closest to the steeping vessel contain freshly steeped grains only at the beginning of the germination stage, while barley close to the kiln is already finished germinating and is in the step of drying.

The malting process itself goes like this: the barley is properly cleaned and then added to a steeping vessel filled with water. The water itself is never changed until shortly before the barley is removed from the steeping vessel. After that, it is moved to a separate vessel called a *couch*, a 2 foot high wooden box.

For taxation reasons (in England, the steeped malt is taxed), barley has to be steeped for at least 40 hours and has to remain at least

26 hours on the couch where its surface is evened out and the exact volume is measured. The tax for a quarter of steeped barley is 21 shillings (= 1 Guinea).

After the steeped barley has remained for 26 hours on the couch, it is moved to field 1, where it is heaped up to 9 inches and turned every 12 hours. After roughly 2 turns rootlets start to appear. From now on, much care is necessary so that the heap doesn't heat up to more than 60 °F (15.5 °C).

Germination itself proceeds rather slow. After about 3 days the first heap is transferred to field 2. On this field, it is treated exactly the same way as on the first field and still must not exceed an internal temperature of 60 °F. At this point, more of the rootlets start appearing and a good amount of condensation starts appearing on the grains. After 3 to 4 more days, the first heap is moved to field 3 where the treatment only changes insofar as the heap size is now down to 3 to 4 inches and turned every 8 to 14 hours depending on the malting floor's temperature. In this field, the acrospire makes the most progress in growing, and it should grow as far to the other end of the grain as possible without starting to grow out of it. It is a principle in England that the acrospire needs to develop as much as possible to effect a complete dissolution within the grain.

After 4 days, the heap is moved to field 4, which is usually the last one. Here, the drying process begins, as the rootlets start to wilt. At this stage, the total process has taken 12 days already and the grain should be fully modified. If that's not the case, the maltster is allowed to sprinkle water on top of it. This is strictly prohibited before the 12 days, as otherwise the maltster could take the grain off the steeping vessel too early and then sprinkle water on the grains later. After sprinkling, the grain is kept at a warmer temperature, but never above 70 to 75 °F (21 to 24 °C).

After 3 more days, i.e. a total of 15 days, germination should be completed. The heap of malted barley should be near the kiln at this stage, upon which it is then placed. On the kiln, the malt is heaped up 9 to 12 inches high and is only turned only twice a day. The kiln temperature should usually be at 80 °F (26 °C), but should never exceed 100 °F (38 °C). After 3 days, the malt should be fully kilned and have attained a pale yellow colour.

English maltsters claim that the malt must not be turned too often, because otherwise moisture on the surface of the heap would come to the bottom and remain in the malt for longer while it is on the kiln. The fuel used is coke or hard coal which are burnt directly under the kilning floor and whose heat directly touches the malt, which can leave behind a slight smell of sulphur in the malt.

(Source: [22, pp. 49–51])

Bohemian Method

In Prague, the following malting method is used in order to extract less from the grains as well as to malt faster.

Steeping is only slightly different from the English method: the barley is steeped only 24 hours, after which it is moved to the malting floor, heaped up 4 to 5 feet high in a conical shape, and sprinkled every 30 minutes with water as well as turned.

After 23 hours, the barley is again moved to the steeping vessel and steeped there for 6 to 8 hours. After this time, it should be sufficiently steeped.

While the barley is heaped up, the next batch can be steeped and then removed from the steeping vessel just before the previous batch is added to it. This way, more barley can be steeped. Practice has shown that this method, when using the same water and steeping at the same temperature, starts germination more quickly. The remainder of the method is the same as the conventional Bavarian method.

(Source: [22, p. 53])

Viennese Method

Compared to the conventional (Bavarian) method, the barley is steeped for a shorter time period. Even at the coldest time in winter, it should only be steeped for 50 to 60 hours. The typical indicators that it is sufficiently steeped cannot be described, the barley instead needs to be inspected closely on the malting floor whether the grain has enough moisture for the post-steeping and whether the acrospire grows slow or quickly.

When the grain is removed from the steeping vessel, it is heaped 2 feet high so that it doesn't dry out immediately and can instead undergo the *post-steeping*, not unlike in the *couch* in the English method. This heap is then turned every 24 hours, usually only twice, until germination has started. With every turn, the size of the heap is lowered, so that it ends up at 3 inches after the final turn. By that time, it should have started showing rootlets.

At this stage, uttermost care needs to be taken that the heap doesn't warm up and that the acrospire doesn't grow too quickly, which is usually caused by too much heat inside the heap.

The heap is then getting turned constantly. The time between turns cannot be pre-determined, but rather needs to be adjusted according to the outside temperature. During spring and autumn, it often needs to be turned every 3 to 4 hours, while in the winter, a turn every 5 to 6 hours should be sufficient.

The grain is considered to have sufficiently germinated when the acrospire has almost broken through the husk. At this point, the endosperm, when rubbed between two fingers, needs to fall apart into just flour. The length of the rootlets is not observed at all, but they should just remain as short as possible.

The following rules are considered to be the most important ones:

1. the heap initially needs to be high enough to allow more steeping even after the grain has been removed from the steeping vessel.
2. the dissolution (modification) of the grain needs to be done slowly, which is done through low heap sizes and turning it more often.
3. the barley should not be steeped for too long, so as not extract too much from it at this stage.

In this process, it can often take 10 to 12 days during winter, but rarely ever less than 8 days, to get to a state of sufficient germination. This process takes more time, but also requires more space. Experts can get an idea what colossal rooms need to be available for that, e.g. at Dreher's brewery in Schwechat near Vienna, or in the brewery in Liesing near Vienna, where in each of these breweries, at least 300,000 Eimer of beer are brewed every year, and all the malt for it is produced on site.

(Source: [22, pp. 53–55])

Air-Dried Malt (Luftmalz)

Air-dried malt (*Luftmalz*, lit. *air malt*) is simply malt that has been dried sufficiently on the drying floor so that it doesn't require any further drying on the kiln.

This type of malt is mainly used for brewing white beer. It is also used to brew vinegar, in particular to give it a colour as pale as wine vinegar. It should generally be preferable to any kilned malt, but also comes with a number of disadvantages for brewing:

1. it is very pale.

2. a very large location would be required to even produce the amount of air-dried malt that would be required, even under optimal circumstances.
3. air-dried malt is harder to mash in.
4. it is harder to draw off wort from a mash from air-dried malt.

(Source: [22, pp. 61–62])

3.12   Hermann Pfauth (1870)

The steeping vessel is filled almost halfway with water. Then barley is added under constant stirring until the steeping vessel is filled up to 1 foot below the edge. In this case this water won't be over the level of the barley yet, so more water is added until the barley is covered by 1/2 a foot of water.

This is now left to rest for 4 to 6 hours, but it's a good idea to stir it two or three times so that any bad kernels, seeds of weeds, chaff, etc. can float to the top. After this time, any kernels floating on top are skimmed off and the water is drained. The drained water should have a dirty yellow colour from what it extracted from the kernels, it should have a bitter taste and be foamy. If water reservoirs are available, it would also be possible to continuously drain the water and replenish it in a single stream. This should bring any bad kernels more reliably to the surface as well as extract substances from the kernel's husks more quickly.

After the water has been drained, the water is replenished and the barley is left to steep for 24 hours. If any more kernels rise to the top when the barley is stirred, then they're skimmed off as well. This is repeated every 24 hours until the barley has been sufficiently steeped. During the warmer months, the steeping water can take on a foul smell, which is why it will have to be changed every 12 hours during these times.

The total duration of steeping mostly depends on the temperature of the water and the steeping room. During winter, when the water has a temperature of 5 to 6 °C and the steeping room 10 to 12 °C, the barley will be sufficiently steeped after 4 days, while in the warmer times of the year, when the water temperature is 12 to 15 °C and the steeping room temperature 17 to 20 °C, it should be ready within 3 days.

Besides the temperature, other factors can contribute to deviations: barley quality, whether it dried out on the field or was damaged by rain, whether it is old or young, thick- or thin-husked, rich in gluten or starch, and also the water, whether it is hard or soft.

The following indicators can be used to recognise whether the barley has sufficient steeped:

1. when cutting or biting through a steeped kernel, the endosperm should be steeped so far that the centre still has a small dry core.
2. when attempting to bend a kernel over your thumbnail, it should be possible without breaking the kernel.
3. when squeezing a kernel on its pointy ends between thumb and index finger, it shouldn't sting.

Barley that has been steeped so much that the inside forms a spongy mass has been over-steeped. It will later grow quickly and tend to go mouldy. Generally, the rule is valid that steeping should be as short as possible, as it can later be adjusted by sprinkling it with water during the germination phase.

Overly long steeping is not advisable as barley (besides the fact that too much substance that will later be necessary for a good fermentation, including mineral salts, would be extracted), even when grown in the same soil, will usually not steep evenly. Especially lighter kernels that don't float to the top during steeping will steep more quickly than heavier ones. This can be fixed by using a barley sorting machine, which not only helps a brewery to sort out dead kernels in advance, but also to separate barley into lighter and heavier kernels which can then be processed separately.

When the barley has been sufficiently steeped, the water is drained and the barley is left in the steeping vessel for 6 to 8 hours of post-steeping. If this takes too long, the top layer can dry out and start germination earlier which can cause an uneven germination from the very beginning. After this time, the steeping vessel is emptied and then cleaned.

The germination process, which is done so that the barley can form diastase and loosen up, is the same as if a farmer planted it in soil. Sowing time combines several of the conditions required for germination: humidity, a medium temperature of 10 to 15 °C, and absence of light and air. The kernel starts sprouting, and by taking its starch from the endosperm, it will first start growing rootlets. Almost at the same time, it will also start growing the acrospire, which will initially grow underneath the husk until it eventually breaks through on the other side of the tip and, when sufficiently long, will eventually also push through the soil.

The development of the acrospire up to this point is almost exclusively fed from the starchy endosperm. But the brewer interrupts this germination process in order to preserve the starch when the acrospire has reached almost the full length of the grain.

The changes to the endosperm that the brewery wants to achieve are the creation of diastase, to loosen up the grain, the consumption of an excess of protein that is necessary for growing the rootlets (which is what makes them valuable animal feed), or has been turned into a more soluble form.

To have the four main conditions of germination – sufficient humidity, medium temperature, absence of light and air – work together, specific conditions are necessary in the brewery. Humidity is added to the grain through steeping. To ensure the absence of light, sufficient air circulation and a medium temperature, malting floors are used, so that even germination can be ensured through the malting process itself.

Malting floors are arched rooms, usually built half-way underground, often also built so that one is on top of another one, with the lower one below and the top one above the ground. The floor should only be slightly tilted (1 inch per 10 foot) to ensure that water can drain, and should be covered with non-absorbent stones.

Solnhofer or Kelheimer plates, made from Jura marble, have been proven to be the best, but bricks, possibly covered with cement, have also been used successfully. When laying the floor with stone, they need to be put close together and the gaps need to be filled with cement which then needs to be sprinkled with water for 14 days while it's still fresh as well as ironed to flatten it out. If it isn't sprinkled with water during hardening, it will later absorb humidity from the germinating barley and cause issues with the germination process.

The malting floor walls are also covered with stone to a height of 1 foot, to make it easier to clean the malting floor, but also to protect it from damage from the shovel during malting. Since a lot of water evaporates during malting and forms condensation on the wall, gutters need to be put up on the wall at 4 foot height to collect the condensation.

For ventilation, either special ventilation shafts are built, or the windows of the malting floor are used. The windows can be closed with shutters to prevent light from getting into the malting floor but also to regulate the temperature to a certain extent. If the malting floor temperature is influenced too much by the outside temperature, an oven to heat the malting floor can also be installed.

After the barley has been moved to the malting floor, it is heaped up high. It is then spread out using an *Esel* (lit. *donkey*), a long, shovel-like wooden board with a handle and a lead for two to four people to pull it, to end up with a roughly 3 inch high heap that spreads out over about 2/3 of the whole malting floor.

To ensure that all grains have an even contact with air and remain at the same temperature and humidity, the heap gets turned every 8 hours using a flat shovel in 2 movements: first, the top layer is taken off and put on the ground, then the second layer is taken and put on top of the first layer. This task requires some experience, but the main points can be summarised:

Before turning the heap, the sides are taken off and the dry kernels are thrown towards the middle of the heap. Then the whole heap gets turned in 2 movements, as described earlier. The grains needs to be shovelled carefully, with the shovel only covered halfway. The first half shall be put down with a half-turned shovel, while the second half needs to put down with a full turn in a throwing movement so that the grains partially cover the first half, but also land about an inch past it. It is said that *the second throw must fly*.

The maltster needs to form a lane, called *Gasse*, between the old heap and the new heap during turning. This lane needs to be kept clean. The maltster's body position needs to be such that they are stood with one foot in the lane and with half a sole in the heap of grain. When the heap has been fully turned, the sides are shovelled up to bring them to the same height as the middle. Any free kernels on the floor are swept up. To check that the heap is even, a candle can be held in the dark malting floor 1/2 a foot over the heap with the flame covered by hand towards one's face. Any uneven bits should be very easy to recognise that way, but to be sure about this, the heap needs to be looked at from different positions.

If a malting floor is constructed so that it has a warmer and a colder side, then the heap needs to differ in height, in particular it needs to be higher where it is colder, and lower where it is warmer.

Assuming a temperature of the malting floor and the heap of grain of about 12 °C, then the first signs of germination should be noticeable on the grain after 24 to 36 hours. After 8 to 12 more hours, the first rootlet should appear. From this time onward, 2 to 3 rootlets should eventually grow to a length of about half the grain, which can happen at a temperature of 15 °C within 3 days. At this stage, the heap needs to be turned in 3 movements instead of 2.

This is done like this: the top layer is taken off with the full width of the shovel and put down slightly into the lane. The middle layer is then thrown slightly past the first layer, and the bottom layer is then put on top while turning the shovel. Through this manipulation, the cold top layer is moved down in a warmer position and the bottom layer towards the warmer middle, while the middle layer ends up on top too cool down.

As rational as this approach may be, it can be hard for some maltsters to control that all grains end up in the correct position within the new heap where they're meant to be, so some breweries keep turning in 2 movements. What is important here in any case is that the heap's internal temperature remains even within the heap. For this, the sides will be heaped up 1/2 an inch higher than the centre, where the heap is on average 3 inch high.

At this stage, the heap gets turned every 10 to 12 hours, sometimes even every 15 hours, depending on the following observations:

1. a lot of "sweat", i.e. dew-like humidity that can be noticed when putting a hand into the heap of grain, or when putting a shovel into the heap and pulling it out again, drops form on the blade that will run down.
2. a healthy, strong, cucumber-like smell.

3. when stick your hand into the heap, it should feel tightly packed.
4. the internal temperature should be measured in the middle layer of the heap, and should be 17 °C, at most 20 °C.
5. the grains have formed 3 rootlets, partially even a fourth one, which should looked crooked.

When these things have been observed, any further turns should spread out the heap thinner and thinner. At this stage, the grains must not be thrown but rather should slide off the shovel in clumps, otherwise they could lose too much of their moisture. It is important to time the start of this work correctly. If it is being done too early, then not enough "sweat" (condensation) may have formed. If it is started too late though, the temperature of the heap may have risen too much, it may have started smelling bad, the rootlets may have grown straight instead of crooked, and the heap may have dried out. This can be adjusted to a certain extent with a gardener's can to sprinkle water on top, but this needs to be done before turning. This also has the effect of lowering the temperature.

After this, the heap is left to rest for 8 to 10 hours, and the next turn is only done when the internal temperature has risen slightly, but shouldn't be over 22 °C, when the heap is sufficiently humid inside, and also how tightly packed the heap feels.

It needs to be ensured though that the grains aren't getting too tightly packed, which is caused by the rootlets getting entangled with each other, so during the next turn, the malt needs to be disentangled by throwing it up in the air. No clumps should have formed, as this would be an issue during kilning.

The next turns are done the same as the previous, with the only difference that it needs to be ensured that that the heap is slightly lowered with each turn. The heap should eventually cover the whole malting floor.

The turning in general requires punctuality and care. The maltster doesn't only have to keep the hours when the malt needs turning, but also needs to do the turning carefully and cleanly, especially to keep the lane as well as any corners or edges free from any grains. If no care is taken, some of the grains can grow quickly and the acrospire may start pushing through the husk and form a blade of grass.

If the heap had an average temperature of 20 °C during germination, then it should be finished within 8 to 10 days. But the longer germination can be extended, the slower it grows, the better the malt is thought to be. An indicator for that is that the acrospire should be about 3/4 the length of the grain. More important though is the modification of the grain. When breaking up a grain and rubbing the endosperm between the fingers, it should leave behind a chalk-like streak. The endosperm should also easily come off the husk. Typically, this state of modification is reached at the same time when the acrospire has reached the above-mentioned length.

With a slower germination at lower temperatures, this dissolution can happen even earlier, before the acrospire has developed as far as this, while an accelerated germination can cause the acrospire to have grown the full length of the grain without the dissolution happening at the same pace. It is therefore assumed that a slow development of the acrospire extracts a certain amount of substance from the endosperm and thus effects a dissolution of the inside of the grain, while a fast growth is mainly caused by an additional absorption of water.

When the majority of grains have been dissolved sufficiently, the germination process is interrupted by moving the malt to the drying floor. The empty malting floor is then aired, swept up and finally cleaned out with brushes and hot water.

Bohemian Method

The Bohemian method differs from the Bavarian method in that the steeping time is reduced and the germination is done at a lower temperature. At a water temperature of 6 °C, the barley is steeped for about 35 hours. The longest steeping time is 45 hours. After removing the barley from the steeping vessel, it is heaped up 3 foot high and left untouched for 24 hours, and then turned every 12 hours in such a way that it the grain is thrown up.

As soon as rootlets start appearing, the heap is spread out to 3 to 4 inches height. Turning, which is always done in 3 movements in an "airy" way (i.e. by throwing up the grains) depends on the internal temperature which rarely exceeds 15 to 16 °C, and on the appearance of "sweat" of which never too much should develop. The malting floors often have a temperature of 10 °C; if they're warmer, then the heap needs to be turned every 6 hours, sometimes even every 3 hours. Germination takes about 10 to 12 days.

Silesian Method

The malting process in Silesia are identical with the Bavarian one in terms of steeping and internal temperature of the heap, only in the treatment there are slight differences. When rootlets start appearing, the heap is spread out so thin that it can be left untouched for 36 to 40 hours without ever exceeding 20 °C. During this, it starts clumping up so much that it needs to be broken up by foot prior to turning. The turning is done in 4 movements in a particular method that is called *Mischen* (lit. *mixing*). First, the top layer is removed and put into the lane. Then, the old heap is loosened up. After that, the remaining grains are taken with the shovel and thrown sideways, and finally, the grains in the lane are cleaned up towards the new heap. Unlike the germination "in cold sweat" as was described earlier, the method of germinating "in warm sweat" was practised where the heap was allows to reach internal temperatures between 25 and 37 °C.

The point of drying the malt after germination is to remove humidity with which it would otherwise continue growing. For this, it is spread out on a large, well-aired floor with windows all around it at a height of 1 to 3 inches. There, it is turned at least 3 times a day, during warm weather at least 6 times a day to prevent mould from growing.

The turning is done in one movement and the malt is thrown up high. If this drying is continued for 8 to 14 days and continuous turning, then this type of malt is called *Luftmalz* (lit. *air malt*). More recently, this has been reduced to just 3 to 4 days. With (at the time) modern double kilns, this is even completely skipped, especially if the malt has already partially dried in the last steps of germination. In this case, only excess malt is temporarily stored on the drying floor prior to kilning.

Kilning is what completely dries out the malt. Different kiln constructions exist, but the two main types are *Rauchdarren* (lit. *smoke kilns*) and *Luftdarren* (lit. *air kilns*), also called *englische Darren* (lit. *English kilns*). Both have three parts in common, a kilning floor upon which the malt is placed, a middle room which contains the fire tubes and where any rootlets fall into, and finally the fire place.

Smoke kilns are the oldest type of kiln, where the hot air together with smoke permeates the malt. Compared to air kilns, it requires less fuel, but on the other hand leaves behind a smoke flavour in the malt which persists in the beer. Even though it makes the beer less perishable, it also makes it taste rougher. For this reason, fuel needs to be chosen that produces as little gases that would influence the flavour of the malt. Typically this would be beechwood, but for specially constructed kilns, coke can also be used. Resiny wood (pine or fir), hard coal or peat cannot be used.

These disadvantages were the reason to construct a kiln where the kilning floor is warmed but the smoke is vented separately. Kilns of this kind are called air kilns. With these, the fire flows into heating pipes or canals made from clay or sheet iron which then heats up the space underneath the kilning floor as well as directing the smoke towards the chimney. To ensure an even heat, the pipes are closer to the fire place and covered with clay, but located higher when they're close to the chimney.

Newer kilns are constructed in such a way that the heated air and smoke don't directly pass into the heating pipes, but have to go through a horizontal network of pipes that is covered in brickwork, allowing hot air to emanate from many small spaces in between. To prevent malt to fall into this area and to start burning, it is covered with a sheet iron roof. The heating tubes also have a roof-like shape so that anything falling on top of them can glide off.

In early constructions when smoke kilns were replaced by air kilns, the kilning floors were constructed from clay tiles. Since the malt wasn't dried by a steady stream of air, but rather by radiating heat, they were changed to perforated sheet iron (occasionally also copper). Even more useful are the more recently introduced rolled wire meshes.

Kilning floors used to be constructed in such a way that they were shaped similar to a roof. These days, they are always kept flat. Kilns either have one kilning floor (single kiln) or two kilning floors on top of each other (double kiln). The top floor is for taking on freshly dried malt, while on the lower floor, kilning is finished with mostly dried malt.

To allow the hot air to escape and to remove any steam coming from the malt, kilns have a number of tubes near the bottom to allow cold air to enter. These are all covered with little roofs to prevent any kernels from falling into them. The cold air streaming in helps move the hot air towards the vent, allowing for a good draught that quickly removes any steam. Good draught is an important property of a good kiln. If it is not good enough, than it can happen that some of the steam re-condenses on the upper floor and drips back onto the lower kilning floor, which not only slows down the kilning process, but can also form *Glasmalz* (lit. *glass malt*).

The practical kilning process has two goals, namely the drying process and the roasting process. During the drying process, the malt is freed from any humidity through a slowly increasing temperatures from 31 to 62 °C. During the roasting process, the malt is heated up even more at temperatures between 62 and 87 °C where the malt gets roasted and takes on its particular malty aroma. It is important to start drying at a low temperature because at temperatures of 50°C or higher, the core of the kernel would gelatinise, which, if it was dried further, then wouldn't dissolve in water anymore. Such malt, often called *Steinmalz* (lit. *stone malt*) or *Glasmalz* (lit. *glass malt*) because it's hard to mill and looks glassy when broken, not only reduces the amount of extract, but can also cause the wort to be cloudy later. Glass malt can more easily form on simpler kilns, especially if the malt has not been fully dried beforehand. Double kilns cause less of these issues.

The exact kiln times depend on the particular construction and the the malt that gets kilned, whether it's (wet) green malt straight from the malting floor or already pre-dried malt from the drying floor.

Very well-constructed kilns can produce fully kilned malt on the lower floor within 4 to 5 hours, while other double kilns can take a total of 24 hours (12 hours on the lower floor) to get finished malt. With simple kilns, the kilning times are even longer.

Fully kilned malt can be recognised by the following properties:

1. the malt, when bitten into, should make a cracking noise, the starch on the inside should partially come away from the husk and break apart, but should be white and powdery.
2. when rubbing several grains between your hands, any rootlets should come off easily.

In some breweries, where darker beers are brewed, the malt is kilned so that the inside is not completely white but that it has a yellow ring on the outside. For this, the temperature is brought up to 62 to 75 °C when the malt is not fully dried yet (but enough to prevent the formation of glass malt). The heat in combination with the remaining humidity causes this browning. If malt is completely dried, it can be brought up to 100 °C and higher without causing any browning.

A darker malt, *Farbmalz* (lit. *colour malt*) can be added in small amounts to darken the beer. This used to be made on kilns at temperatures of 125 °C or higher. It is nowadays more practical to use roasting drums like they're used for coffee roasting. Often, instead of *Farbmalz*, burnt sugar or syrup are used to adjust the colour of the wort. But it also needs to be mentioned that there is a big difference in flavour if a beer has been brewed from pale malt with a small addition of *Farbmalz* or sugar colouring or if it has been brewed from dark malt. The former tastes more wine-like and slightly burnt, while the latter doesn't have this flavour and instead tastes sweeter and more full-bodied.

Generally, more emphasis on the malting should happen than what is currently done. While the malting, mashing and fermentation methods have an influence on the final beer, the kilning process may have the biggest impact of all of them.

After the malt has been fully kilned, it is spread out to a height of 1 to 2 foot and then crushed with the feet for at least 15 minutes to break off any rootlets still attached to the malt. As this is much easier when the malt is still warm, it is customary in some breweries to already do this step directly on the kiln. This is not practical because it's harder work in such a hot room, and can also damage the kilning floors over a long period. The rootlets are then separated through a malt cleaning machine.

To store the malt properly, all the rootlets need to be removed first, as they would otherwise draw humidity from the air which can have a negative impact on the malt. Then the malt needs to be stored on a dry floor that is not too airy, best in a wooden box where it is heaped up high.

In the past, the opinion used to be prevalent that malt would improve in quality when stored over a longer period of time. This was mostly because the malt was smoke-kilned and long storage would get rid of some of the smoke flavour. With modern kilns, the storage time can be shortened. Typically, malt is stored less than 6 months, but should also not be used before 14 days of storage.

(Source: [23, pp. 51–88])

Chapter 4

Mashing and Brewing Techniques

4.1 Double Decoction

4.1.1 According to P. Müller (1854)

While Müller's book about beer brewing from 1854 is relatively general in its approach, it does put some focus on specific local differences in brewing methods between regions of Germany and Europe. While Müller mentions the use of different forms of decoction mashing in different regions (e.g. two thick decoctions and one thin decoction in Bavaria, three thick decoctions in Bohemia, two thin decoctions in Belgium, etc.), his most general example of decoction mashing is actually a double decoction consisting of two thick decoctions. While it is not specific to Bavarian brewing, we nevertheless document it here as it is referenced in a description of Bavarian triple decoction by the same author later in this book.

In Müller's example, he starts off with a brew kettle sized at 12 badische Ohm (18 hl) and 800 Pfund (400 kg) of malt. The brew kettle is then filled so that it is 3/4 quarters full (i.e. 13.5 hl), while the mash tun is filled with 7.75 to 8 Ohm (11.62 to 12 hl) of cold water. The crushed malt is then mashed in and left to stand for 1 hour. When the water is boiling in the kettle, the mash is stirred through again for 15 minutes, then 3.75 to 4 Ohm (5.625 to 6 hl) of boiling water are slowly poured through the *Pfaffe* (a pipe for underletting water underneath the false bottom) while constantly stirring until the mash has reached a temperature of 28 to 30 °R (35 to 37.5 °C). Müller points out that these ratios assume a grain temperature of 10 °R (12.5 °C) and water at well temperature. Practical conditions, such as winter temperatures, will require the brewer to adjust the overall ratios, and e.g. mash in with less cold and more hot water.

The remaining water is then removed from the kettle and used to clean out other brewing vessels, including coolships and fermenters. When the kettle is empty, 7 Ohm (10.5 hl) of thick mash are transferred to the kettle and brought to a boil. It needs to be stirred so prevent scorching. Müller calls this *erstes Dickmaischekochen* (first thick mash boil). This first boil is meant to last 30 minutes. Ten minutes before the end of it, stirring and mixing the mash in the mash tun shall resume. Then the first thick mash is mixed back and thoroughly mixed in until the main mash has reached a temperature of 42 °R (52.5 °C). If any thick mash remains in the kettle, it can stay there.

This is immediately followed by again moving thick mash from the mash tun to the kettle so that it contains 6.5 to 7 Ohm (9.75 to 10.5 hl) mash in total. It is again brought to a boil under constant stirring and boiled for 30 minutes, the *zweites Dickmaischekochen* (second thick mash boil). As before, stirring and mixing the main mash shall resume 10 minutes before the end of the boil. Then all of the thick mash is scooped back and thoroughly mixed into the main mash. The mash temperature should then be at 60 °R (75 °C). After scooping back has finished, stirring shall continue for another 15 minutes, then it is left to rest for an hour so that it can finish saccharification.

In the meanwhile, the kettle gets cleaned and refilled 3/4 full (i.e. 13.5 hl) with water which is again brought to a boil.

Then lautering commences and the wort is collected in the *Würzbütte* (also called *Brühbütte*) by first drawing it off through a tap into the *Sarg* (a synonym for *Grant*), from where it is then pumped up into the *Würzbütte* [3, p. 190]. The first runnings shall have an extract content of 14 to 15%. When all the wort has been drawn off, an additional 5 Ohm (7.5 hl) of hot water is added, briefly mashed, and more wort is drawn off. This is repeated once more with an amount of 3.25 Ohm (4.875 hl) of hot water. The kettle should now be empty, and the wort from the *Würzbütte* is added to it, followed by the second and third runnings from the subsequent mashes.

After boiling the wort with the hops, the resulting wort shall have an extract content of 11 to 12%.

(Source: [3, pp. 193–208])

4.2 Triple Decoction

4.2.1 According to Benno Scharl (1814)

Benno Scharl's book about brewing Bavarian Brown Beer is probably one of the earliest publications that comprehensively describes Bavarian brewing in all its aspects. When it came to mashing in particular, he emphasised the importance of being able to measure all ingredients involved, and determining the volume of all involved vessels was the first step to it, whether it was the brewing kettle, the mash tun, the coolship, the fermenters or the casks. In the description of the whole brewing process, this allowed him to exactly measure and describe the shrinkage of liquid, starting with the brewing water to the wort or beer at all the stages, from brewing to fermentation and lagering to sales.

He starts off with a sample brew of Winterbier. It is brewed from 7 Schäffel (1556 l) of dried malt and 18 Pfund (10.103 kg) of hops. The total amount of water used in the mash tun and the brew kettle were 115 Eimer and 45.44 Maß (7916 l). The mashing process consisted of two thick decoctions and one final thin decoction, mash-out and lautering. The resulting sweet wort had a volume of 83 Eimer and 10.432 Maß (5689 l).

After boiling the wort with the hops, a total of 64 Eimer and 30.528 Maß (4411 l) of wort were received on the coolship. After cooling, the wort volume was at 62 Eimer and 1.528 Maß (4243 l). Then the wort was transferred to fermenters, where the total volume was 61 Eimer and 24.576 Maß (4199 l). After primary fermentation, the beer was moved to lagering casks, where a total volume of 59 Eimer and 50.048 Maß (4090 l) of green beer was received. After lagering, a total of 52 Eimer and 5.056 Maß (3563 l) was sold [9, pp. 98–99].

The mashing process itself is described as follows [9, pp. 99–107]:

The first step is called *Einmaischen* (mashing in). The mash tun is filled with cold water, and the crushed malt is added and mixed into the water using special mash paddles, called *Maischschaufel* (lit. "mash shovel") or *Scheiter* (a term nowadays used for logs of wood). This is done until all malt is mixed in well, and no more clumps or dry bits can be found in the mash. This cold mash is then left to stand for 3 to 4 hours.

Water is then brought to a boil in the kettle, and as soon as its boils vigorously, it can be scooped over the cold mash while the mash itself gets thoroughly mixed through. This step is described as involving all brewers, some scooping the boiling water, while others mixing the whole mash. Scharl emphasises that the mash paddle needs to be moved in a certain way: it needs to be pushed all the way to the bottom of the mash tun, then pulled towards you, then turned, and then pulled up, to ensure a thorough and even mixing. This mixing operation is done until all the boiling water has been mixed into the mash.

Then the mash, in particular as much of the malt, is scooped over into the kettle until it is full. This is the first thick mash in the kettle which is then brought to a boil. While it is heating up, it needs to be stirred initially to prevent the malt from scorching on the bottom of the kettle. At a certain point, this is not necessary anymore, as "the malt lifts itself up" as Scharl describes it. When the mash has reached the boil, the fire is turned down to prevent overboiling. This first mash shall then boil for 90 minutes.

After the first thick mash has boiled for this duration, it is then again scooped back into the main mash and mixed in, using the same technique as described earlier. When the mashing is finished, it is left to rest for about 15 minutes. The whole process is then repeated: again, the mash is scooped over to the kettle until it is full, again brought to a boil, and after the boil, scooped back and mixed into the main mash.

Thirty minutes before the second thick mash is mixed back, 3 Eimer (205 l) of wort are drawn from the main mash into the *Grand*, a vessel underneath the mash tun tap used to collect wort. After the kettle has been emptied of all the thick mash and any hard matter has been removed from it, this wort is added to the kettle to prevent the inside surface from burning.

After the second thick mash, the mash is left to rest for 30 minutes, after which the tap is opened and the *Lautermaisch*, the final thin mash, is drawn off into the *Grand*. It is scooped from there to the kettle, where it is then brought to a boil. As soon as it starts boiling, it is scooped back into the main mash and mixed in as described earlier. As this is the final mash, the mixing operation is done for a longer period of time of at least 30 minutes. The mash is then left to rest for 1 to 2 hours.

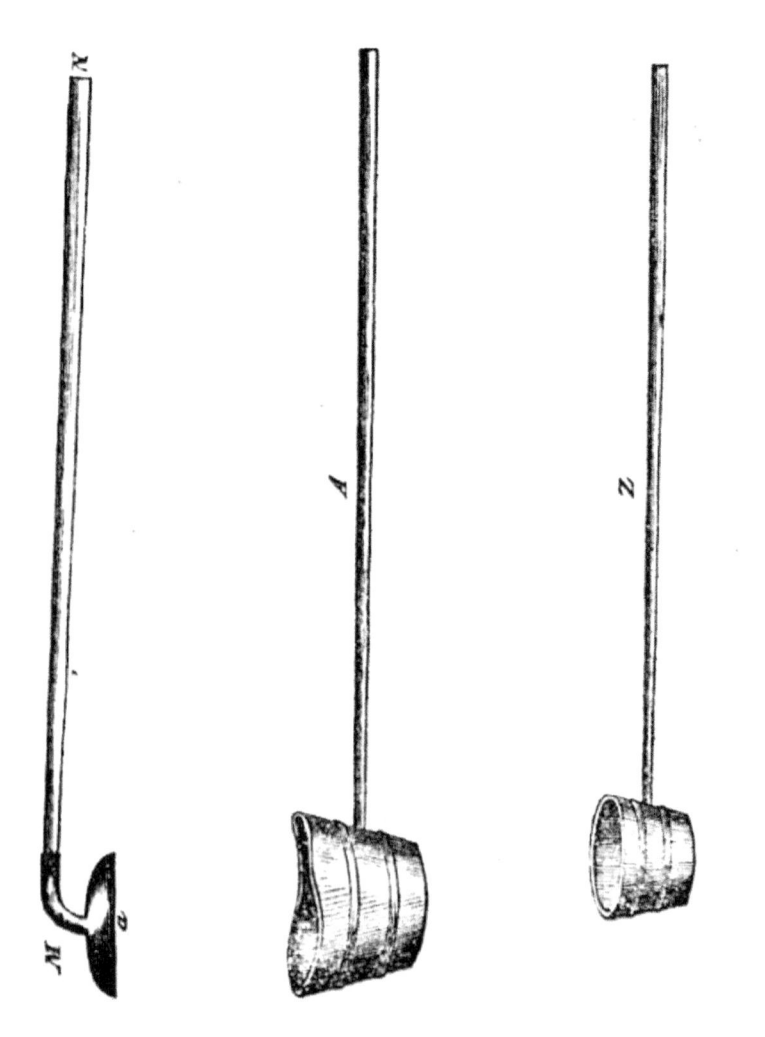

From left to right: thick mash stirrer, mash scoop, wort scoop [18]

In the meanwhile, more water is brought to a boil in the kettle, to be used for sparging (*anschwänzen*) of the *Nachbier*, for washing the coolship and for cleaning any other brewing vessels.

When the mash has finished resting, lautering is then started, and the wort is drawn off from the tap into the *Grand*. This needs to be done carefully, and the wort needs to be clear. At the same time, any hot water from the kettle needs to be scooped out, so that the wort can be scooped from the *Grand* into the kettle. The hops are then added to the kettle as well. The hops then need to boil with just relatively little wort for at least 15 minutes. After this time period, more wort is added to the kettle, where it is then left to boil for another 60 to 90 minutes.

After the boil, the wort is then scooped onto a hop strainer that holds back any hops, and then moved to the coolship where it is left to cool.

As soon as the first runnings have all been drawn off from the mash tun, the *Nachbier* mashing begins: first, the top layer of the mash, the *Oberteig* (lit. "upper dough") is removed with a shovel and used for the production of distilled spirits. The mash is then turned over and hot water is added in a quantity depending on how much *Nachbier* shall be made. This is then left to rest for 30 minutes, until the mash tun tap is again opened to collect the second runnings in the *Grand*. This wort is boiled either in the kettle or, if available, a smaller kettle dedicated to the *Nachbier*. For hopping, the hops used in the first boil and recovered in the hop strainer are reused. After the boil, the wort is strained in the same way as the first runnings and then moved to a second coolship.

Scharl estimates that from every *Schäffel* of malt, 30 to 40 Maß of *Nachbier* can be made.

After the *Nachbier* wort has been drawn off, more water is added and mixed through, about 16 to 18 Eimer (1094 to 1231 l). After 30 minutes of resting, the third runnings, called *Glattwasser*, are drawn off. This *Glattwasser* is also used in the production of distilled spirits, by mixing it with the *Oberteig*, harvested yeast, hot break from the coolship and other waste from the brewing process to then ferment to later be distilled.

The spent grains are shovelled out of the mash tun and then used or sold as animal feed. Underneath the false bottom, some hard matter will also have collected. This *Unterteig* is also removed and used together with the *Oberteig* for distillation.

In order to cool the wort in the coolships, a "crutch" on a long stick is used to beat the wort. This takes 8 to 10 hours and forms a thick foam. It is important to note here that at the time, coolships were still made from wood. While Scharl describes the beating of the wort as a common technique, he also considers it to be unnecessary and in fact counterproductive, as the thick foam would actually prevent the wort from cooling. At the time of writing, he had stopped using this technique for 9 years, and had observed that the wort will cool down to the right temperature about 2 to 3 hours earlier, provided the coolship has enough of a draught to cool both from the top and the bottom.

Wooden coolship at the Franconian brewery museum in Bamberg

Cooling is finished when the wort has reached a temperature of 10° Réaumur or 12.5°C. The wort is then transferred to the fermenters. At very cold temperatures during the winter, this transfer can also start at a wort temperature of 11° Réaumur or 13.75°C.

The *Nachbier* is treated the same way as the main beer. Any hot break that has collected in the coolships is again used for distillation.

Scharl also notes that if wort is cooling during a thunderstorm, the cooler shall be closed up as the light from the flash allegedly damages the beer.

One issue with Benno Scharl's account is that, even though he emphasised exact measurements and calibration of all brewing vessels, did not provide us with specific volumes during brewing. While he mentioned how much beer could be brewed from a set amount of malt and hops, there is no mention of expected or observed volumes of mash or liquid in the mash tun or the kettle. Temperatures are only mentioned for the wort, but not for any stage of the mashing process itself. While it confirms the use of triple decoction mashing, it makes it hard to exactly reproduce the whole process without further knowledge or experimentation.

4.2.2 Bavarian Method According to Friedrich Meyer (1830)

This description [1, pp. 105–114] starts off with talking about how much water to use for brewing: to brew Winterbier from 7 Schäffel (1156 l) of dry malt or 8 Schäffel 1 Metze (1815 l) of conditioned malt, 115 Eimer (7867 l) of water are necessary. If the *Haustrunk* ("house drink") for brewers is subtracted, this should still yield 49 Eimer (3352 l) of beer. The amount of "house drink" is not specified, though. The kettle shall be filled completely with water, while the remaining amount shall be put in the mash tun. The crushed malt is then added to the mash tun and mixed well using mash paddles. This is called *Einmaischen* (mashing in) or *Einteigen* (doughing in).

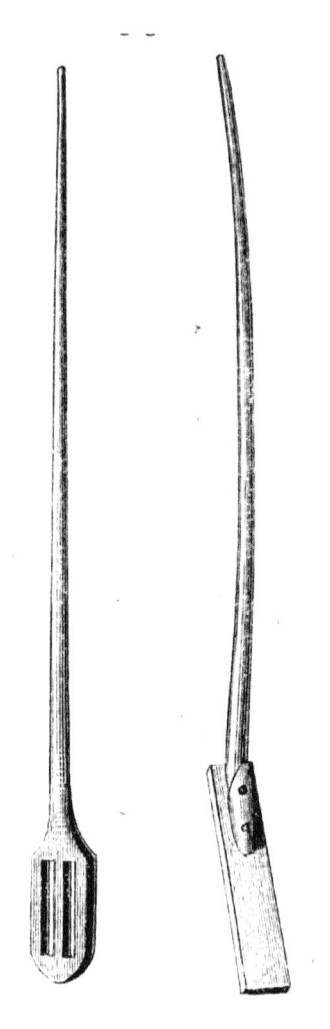

Brewing is described to generally happen at night. According to Meyer, mashing in usually happens at 8pm. The cold mash is then left to rest for 3 to 4 hours. During this time, the water in the kettle is brought to a boil so that the water is boiling by 11pm or 12pm.

The boiling water is then scooped over into the mash tun by two brewers, during which the other brewers thoroughly mix through the mash. This is done in a particular way: the mash paddles are pushed on the bottom of the mash tun towards the centre of it, from where it is again dragged back on the bottom towards the edge, where it is then pulled up and twisted. This is called *aufwedeln*. Before the kettle is completely empty, the fire needs to be dampened to prevent it from getting damaged.

Two types of mash paddles [20]

With all the hot water in the mash tun, mashing stops. The brewers then start scooping back thick mash into the kettle until it is almost full. To make it easier to scoop the thick mash over, a temporary gutter called *Überziehrinne* is installed. The fire is then again lit underneath the kettle, the mash is brought to a boil and then boiled for 1.5 hours. Before it starts boiling, it needs to be thoroughly stirred to prevent scorching, and also during the boil to prevent boil overs. The brewer responsible for the kettle, called *Pfannenknecht* or *Oberknecht*, must keep an eye on the kettle at all times during the boil.

After the boil is finished, the fire is again dampened, and the boiled decoction is scooped back into the mash tun and thoroughly mixed through. Directly afterwards, the kettle is again filled with thick mash, and again boiled like the first thick mash, but only for one hour. While the second thick mash is boiling, 3 to 4 Eimer (205 to 273 l) of clear wort are drawn off through the mash tun's tap into the *Grand*. The wort is scooped back into the mash tun until it runs clear. When the boil has finished, the mash is again scooped back into the mash tun and thoroughly mixed in. When kettle is empty, it is cleaned with a bit of water, and the wort in the *Grand* is scooped into the kettle. During this time, the mixing in the mash tun continues for a total of 30 minutes. Afterwards, it is left to rest for 15 minutes.

After this rest, the tap is again opened and wort is drawn off and scooped into the kettle until it is full. This is called the *Lautermaische*. It is then brought to a boil. As soon as it's started boiling, it is scooped back into the mash and mixed in thoroughly for about 30 minutes. When the scooping back is finished, the kettle is filled with water to heat it up as sparge water for *Nachbier* as well as cleaning purposes.

After the mashing is finished, the mash tun is left to rest for 1.5 hours. During this rest, other works around the brewery can be performed such as weighing out the hops. After this rest, wort is slowly drawn off. It is scooped back until it runs clear. While the wort is running off into the *Grand*, the kettle is emptied and cleaned out. The wort is then scooped from the *Grand* into the kettle, which is called *hacken* or *einschlagen*. This is done until the kettle is full.

During the scooping over of the wort, the hops are added to the kettle. When the kettle is almost full, the fire is again lit and the wort is boiled for an hour. At the end of the boil, the wort is then scooped onto the coolship through a hop strainer.

While the wort is boiling with the hops, the top layer of the mash, called *Oberteig*, is removed and put aside. Then the mash is mixed with shovels, followed by pouring over hot water to get wort for *Nachbier*. After adding the hot water, the mash is against mixed through and left to rest for 30 minutes, until the wort is drawn off and boiled in a small separate kettle together with some of spent hops from the hop strainer. After the boil, the wort is cooled in a small separate coolship and then fermented.

An additional round of sparging, which is done exactly the same way as in the previous step, produces *Glattwasser* which is used to produce distilled spirits. The spent grains are then removed and used as animal feed. The bottom layer, called *Unterteig* or *Bodenteig*, is washed out from the mash tun and together with the *Oberteig* and the *Glattwasser* is also used for distilling.

4.2.3 Method of Brewing in Munich According to David Booth (1834)

This account of the Munich brewing method from 1834 is based on information David Booth received from "two German brewers (from Vienna and Munich)" [24, p. iv]. Although not mentioned by name, these two brewers were Anton Dreher and Gabriel Sedlmayr the Younger, who both spent time in England and Scotland from July 1833 until early 1834 and personally met David Booth. As this account is from an English book, the units used are British Imperial units, accompanied by the equivalent amount in metric units. Only temperatures have been converted to Celsius.

The two vessels used for brewing are a kettle and a mash tun. The mash tun is equipped with a false bottom made from copper and perforated with holes. To move liquid from the kettle to the mash tun or vice versa, a movable wooden trough is placed both vessels.

For one brew, 8 quarters (2,326.37 litres) of malt and 8 pounds of Bavarian or Bohemian hops are used to brew 27 barrels (4,416.5 litres) of Summer Beer (which the author calls a *keeping beer*).

Initially, the mash tun is filled with 38 barrels (6,215.8 litres) of cold water, and the kettle with 19 barrels (3,107.9 litres) of water which are brought to a boil. The 8 quarters of malt are added to the mash tun and are stirred in until they're completely mixed. The mash is then left to stand for 4 hours.

Then the boiling water is poured over the mash which gets mashed through, which should raise the temperature of the mash to 40°C. As soon as the kettle is empty, it gets refilled with a thick portion of the mash, 17 or 18 barrels (2,780.7 resp.

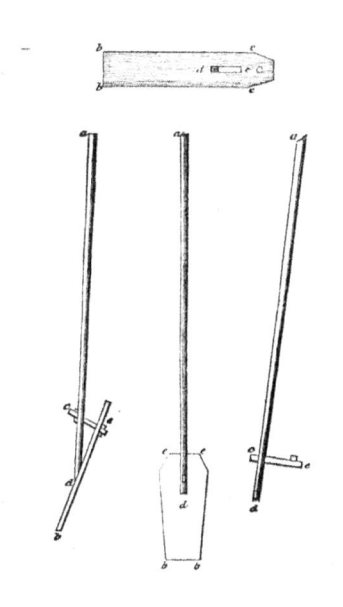

A Munich mash paddle [18]

2,944.3 litres) in volume, which is nearly a third of the overall volume. The mash in the kettle is then brought to a boil, and will boil for an hour during which it will sweeten and acquire a browner colour. It is then mixed back into the mash under constant stirring, which should raise the mash temperature to 55°C.

Immediately after emptying the kettle, it is again refilled with a thick portion of the mash, the same volume as before, 17 or 18 barrels. It is again brought to a boil, this time boiled for 30 minutes, and then returned to the mash tun and mixed through. This should increase the mash temperature to 67°C.

For the third and final mash, only thin mash is taken, as the grains will have partially fallen down in the mash tun. Of thin mash, 15 barrels (2,453.6 litres) are taken and moved to the kettle, accompanied by 2 barrels (327.1 litres) of wort run off through the mash tun's tap. This liquid should be nearly clear and needs to be boiled for 15 minutes before it is returned to the mash tun and mixed in. The final temperature the mash reaches should then be 75°C.

The bottom of the kettle is then covered with water to prevent it from burning. The mash tun is then left to rest for an hour, during which the grain should settle and leave a clear wort behind. Then lautering begins, where the wort is drawn off from the mash through the false bottom and the tap. This wort is immediately added to the kettle and mixed with 60 pounds (27.18 kg) of hops. When all the wort is drained, the top layer of grey slime is taken off from the drained mash, and 3 barrels (490.7 litres) of boiling water are sprinkled over the mash and left to rest for 15 minutes. Then the second runnings are drawn off and added to the kettle. For the final runnings, the same is done with 6 barrels (981.4 litres) of boiling water, but these runnings are only used later in the distillery.

The wort in the kettle is then boiled for 2.5 to 3 hours, cooled down in coolers, and moved to the fermenting vessels at a temperature of 7°C. Then bottom-fermenting yeast is added, at a quantity of 6 to 7 gallons (27.3 resp. 31.8 litres). Fermentation takes about 10 to 12 days, after which the beer is moved to large lagering casks sized at 12 to 16 barrels (1,962.9 resp. 2,617.2 litres) in which it will mature for 8 to 10 months. To serve beer, it is drawn off from large casks into smaller serving casks and served on the same day. This type of beer is Summer Beer, and is only brewed from December to February and drunk during the summer months up to November.

In addition, Winter Beer is brewed using mostly the same method. Only 36 pounds (16.3 kg) are used, but using the same amount of malt, 31 gallons (5,070.8 litres) of winter beer can be brewed. The wort with the hops is only boiled for 1.5 hours. The fermented beer is only matured for 8 to 10 days, after which it is filled into barrel-sized casks (163.6 litres) which have been pre-filled with about 4 gallons (18.2 litres) of half-fermented beer straight from the fermenters. Fermentation restarts and continues for about 8 to 10 days, after which the cask is brought to the publican's cellar. Secondary fermentation continues in the cellar for another 2 weeks, after which it is closely bunged. After 4 or 5 more days, the beer is ready to serve. It should be bright as wine and be highly carbonated [24, pp. 25–29].

4.2.4 Bavarian Brewing Method According to A. Herrmann (1839)

In Herrmann's description [13, pp. 44–47], the mash tun is filled with cold water into which the crushed malt is mashed in, and mixed so thoroughly that no clumps of dry malt remain. The kettle, also filled with water, is heated up and brought to a boil. The cold mash is left to rest for 3 to 4 hours, during which the water in the kettle has time to come up to temperature. In cold temperatures, the mash can be left another 1 to 2 hours more, but this is not advisable in warmer weather as the cold mash may start to ferment.

When the water is boiling, the so-called *Anlauben* starts, which consists of hot water getting scooped over the cold mash while all brewers are thoroughly mixing through the mash, according to a particular method: the mash paddle is put as close to the centre of the mash tun as possible, pushed down to the bottom of it, and then pulled towards the brewer, then twisted to lift the malt mass, and then pulled upwards. This is continued until all water has been mixed in. After this mashing procedure the mash should have a temperature of 32 to 33 °R (40 to 41.25 °C).

Now the first thick mash is scooped over into the kettle. The mash scooped over needs to be as thick as possible to contain the maximum amount of malt. This is done until the kettle is full, the remaining mash is left in the mash tun. The fire under the kettle is then stirred to bring the mash to a boil. The mash in the kettle needs to be stirred to prevent it from scorching until it "lifts itself up" from the bottom of the kettle. When the first thick mash is boiling, the fire can be closed a bit, and the mash is left to boil for 1.5 hours.

When this is finished, the boiled mash is scooped back into the mash tun and thoroughly mixed in. Just before that, 3 Eimer (205 l) of thin mash are collected in the *Grand* to cover the kettle after it's been emptied. This second mashing should be done like the first mash and be conducted until everything from the kettle has been scooped over and mixed in. The collected thin mash in the *Grand* is then added to the kettle. After this, the mash temperature shall be at 42 to 45 °R (52.5 to 56.25 °C). The mash is then left to rest for 15 minutes.

After this rest, mash is again scooped over from the mash tun to the kettle. This second decoction can be thinner than the first one. It is again brought to a boil, and scooped back into the mash tun and thoroughly mixed through. This mashing should last 30 minutes, followed by a rest of 15 minutes. After this rest, thin mash shall be drawn into the *Grand* to fill the kettle. This is the so-called *Lautermaische* which gets boiled and then scooped back into the mash tun and again mixed in for at least 30 minutes. The final temperature of the mash shall be at 60 to 64 °R (75 to 80 °C).

As soon as the *Lautermaische* has been completely scooped out of the kettle, it is filled with water to heat it up to be used as sparge water for *Nachbier* but also for cleaning purposes.

The mash is left to rest for 1.5 to 2 hours. During this time other preparations such as weighing out the hops can be done. After this rest, wort is drawn off until it is clear and then scooped into the emptied kettle. If the bottom of the kettle is covered with wort, the hops are added and boiled for 30 minutes. Only after that, the remaining wort is scooped into the kettle. This wort is boiled for 1.5 hours, then strained through a hop strainer and put on a coolship.

4.2.5 Bavarian Method According to Lorenz Zierl (1843)

In this description [17, pp. 21–27], actual brewing begins with crushing the malt. This begins with conditioning the malt, called *Einsprengen*. The uncrushed malt is wetted with water, at a rate of about 15 Maß of water per Schäffel of malt. 6 Metzen of dry malt shall result in 7 Metzen of conditioned malt. Duty to be paid on a Schäffel of conditioned malt are 5 Gulden. After conditioning, the malt is then crushed. It is expected that 6 Metzen of malt should result in 8.25 Metzen of crushed malt. 100 volumes dry malt should therefore result in 116 conditioned and 137 volumes crushed malt. The crushed malt should then be used within the next 6 to 8 hours.

The first step of mashing is mashing in. This happens in the mash tun that has previously been filled with water. The amount of water needed to mash in a Schäffel (222 l) of malt is 9 Eimer (615 l) cold water. In terms of volumes, the expected ratio of water to crushed malt is 202 volumes of water to 100 volumes of crushed malt. After all the malt has been mixed in, the cold mash is left to stand for 4 to 6 hours. During this time, water is heated up in the kettle. The volume of water in the kettle depends on the type of beer being brewed, i.e. Schenkbier or Lagerbier.

It was prescribed by Bavarian law how much beer could be brewed from a Schäffel of malt, in particular 7 Eimer (478 l) of Schenkbier or 6 Eimer (410 l) of Lagerbier.

The volumes of water required for mash in and first mash required for brewing with 100 volumes of malt are shown in this table:

Mash Step	Schenkbier	Lagerbier
Mash In	202.3	202.3
First Mash	173.0	130.0
Total	375.3	232.3

These ratios may differ by brew-house, though. With the water heated up, it is scooped into the mash tun and thoroughly mixed in. This is continued until the mash has reached a temperature of 30 to 31 °R (37.5 to 38.75 °C). When this temperature is reached, the thick part of the mash is scooped from the mash tun to the kettle. The total volume of this first thick decoction should be about half of the water volume used. The decoction is then brought to a boil and boiled for some time. The exact time depends on the brew-house, but times between 45 and 90 minutes are common.

When this boil has finished, it is scooped back into the mash tun and thoroughly mixed in, until the mash has reached a temperature of 45 °R (56.25 °C). Immediately afterwards, the thick part of the mash is again scooped back into the kettle, at about the same volume as the first decoction and boiled for 30 to 45 minutes. After this time has passed, it is again scooped into the mash tun and mixed in until the mash temperature rises to 54 °R (67 °C). After mixing through for 15 to 30 minutes, the thin part of the mash is scooped into the mash tun, either from the top of the mash or by drawing it off through the false bottom. This thin mash is again boiled for some time, the exact time depending on the brew-house, it is scooped back and mixed into the mash so that it reaches a final temperature of 62 to 65 °R (77.5 to 81.25 °C). After mixing for another 15 minutes, the mash tun is then covered and left to rest for 60 to 90 minutes.

After this rest, the valves are opened and wort is collected in the *Grand*. It is scooped back into the mash tun until it runs clear. The clear wort is then scooped into the kettle. This is called *Hacken*. When all the wort has been collected, the top layer of the mash, the so-called *Oberteig* is removed, and then *Anschwänzwasser* (sparge water) is poured on top of the mash to get a lower gravity wort that is either turned into a *Nachbier* or used to produce vinegar or distilled spirits. Any runnings received from an additional application of *Anschwänzwasser* are called *Glattwasser* and are also used together with the *Oberteig* and the *Unterteig* to produced distilled spirits. The spent grains are used as animal feed.

The wort is moved to the kettle, brought to a boil and boiled with a particular quantity of hops. The boil duration can vary. The longer it boils, the more water evaporates, and the more aromatic oil from the hops also evaporate. After the boil, the wort is strained through a hop strainer and put in a coolship.

There, the wort is cooled to a temperature of 8 to 10 °R (10 to 12.5 °C). These wooden coolships should be kept away from any sunlight and shall receive a good enough draught of air so that the wort can cool quickly enough.

4.2.6 Bavarian Brewing Method According to Friedrich Meyer (1847)

Friedrich Meyer vastly expanded his previous work [1] in its fourth edition [11] which included brewing descriptions that were more comprehensive and precise than in previous versions of his book.

As with Meyer's previous description, this one [11, pp. 145–160] starts off with the amount of water required to brew beer. The amount of malt that needs to be used to brew a certain amount of beer was defined by Bavarian law at the time. From a Schäffel (222 l) of dry malt, 7 Eimer (478 l) of Winterbier or Schenkbier or 6 Eimer (410 l) of Sommerbier or Lagerbier could be brewed. Since the malt was typically conditioned before crushing, the amounts of beer to brew from a Schäffel of conditioned malt were 6 Eimer (410 l) of Winterbier/Schenkbier and 5 1/7 Eimer (351 l) of Sommerbier/Lagerbier. To brew this amount of beer, a total of 14 Eimer (957 l) of water are required for Winterbier/Schenkbier, or 13 Eimer (889 l) of water for Sommerbier/Lagerbier.

This amount of water is divided between the mash tun and the kettle, with the larger amount going into the kettle. Meyer recommends to measure the volumes of the water and the mash at all steps of the brewing process, but does not specify a particular ratio between mash tun and kettle.

Brewing itself starts by mashing in the crushed malt with the cold water. Brewing starts in the evening, at 8 to 9 pm. After mashing in, the mash is left to rest for 3 to 6 hours. If it's cold, it can easily rest for up to 6 hours, but at slightly warmer temperatures, it shouldn't rest for longer than 4 hours. During this rest, the kettle with water shall be brought to a boil. This should ideally be timed so that the water is boiling at the time when the cold mash has rested long enough.

Then the first mashing begins: all brewers, which according to Meyer should be at least 6 people, need to be present. Two of the brewers start scooping hot water from the kettle into the mash tun, while the others mix the mash thoroughly using mash paddles. The mashing is done in a particular way: the mash paddle is constructed from a thick handle at the end of which a thin wooden board of a length of 2 Schuh (about 60 cm) and a width of 1/2 Schuh (about 15 cm) is attached. It is put towards the middle of the mash tun. The brewer then drags it on the bottom of the mash tun towards himself, then twists it and pulls it up at the same time to lift up the malt and agitate it as much as possible.

Mashing and scooping over hot water is continued until the thermometer in the mash tun shows a mash temperature of 33 to 34 °R (41.25 to 42.5 °C). The mixing then immediately stops, and thick mash is scooped from the mash tun into the kettle until it is half full. The remaining mash is kept in the mash tun.

The thick mash in the kettle is then brought to a boil. It needs to be stirred to prevent scorching. For that, a special rake made from copper with a wooden handle is used. When the mash is boiling, the same rake is used to push the mash around to prevent it from boiling over. The total boil time of the thick mash is mentioned to be 1.5 hours.

At the end of the boil, the boiling mash is scooped back into the mash tun while the brewers thoroughly mix the mash. This is continued until the mash in the mash tun has reached a temperature of 44 to 45 °R (55 to 56.25 °C). Immediately, the thick mash is again scooped from the mash tun back into the kettle until it is about 2/3 full. This second thick mash is again brought to a boil and boiled for 45 minutes to 1 hour.

During this time, several Eimer of wort are drawn off from the mash tun into the *Grand* to use it to cover the kettle as soon as the second thick mash has been fully scooped out. This is to prevent any damages from the heat on the kettle.

After the end of the second boil, the thick mash is again scooped back into the mash tun while the brewers mix it thoroughly. The mashing continues for another 30 minutes after the scooping back has finished. Scooping back should be stopped when the mash in the mash tun has reached a temperature of 53 to 54 °R (66.25 to 67.5 °C). The kettle in the meanwhile gets rinsed out.

After mashing has finished, the mash is left to rest for 15 minutes. Then, wort is drawn off from the mash tun into the *Grand* and from there scooped into the kettle. This is called *hacken* or *einschlagen*. This is continued until the kettle is about 3/4 full or however much is necessary to later bring the mash to a final temperature of 62 to 64 °R (77.5 to 80 °C). The wort in the kettle is called *Lautermaisch* or *Dünnmaisch*, and immediately is brought to a boil. As soon as it has reached a full boil, it is scooped back into the mash tun while the brewers thoroughly mix it in to reach the aforementioned target temperature. At no point shall the mash temperature go over the maximum temperature of 64 °R (80 °C), while undershooting the temperature range by a few degrees is less of an issue. According to Meyer, experienced brewers can estimate the temperature of the mash just purely on the filling level of the mash tun.

When scooping the *Lautermaisch* back has finished, the kettle again gets cleaned and filled with however much hot water is later needed for making *Nachbier* and cleaning the brewing vessels. The mash tun is then covered and the mash is left to rest for two hours. This time can be used to do other work and preparations around the brew house, such as weighing out the hops for later.

After the rest, wort is then slowly drawn off into the *Grand*. Any wort is scooped back into the mash tun until it runs clear. While the wort is drawn off, the hot water in the kettle is moved to other vessels. The wort from the *Grand* is then pumped or scooped into the kettle. This is continued until all the wort has been drawn off. As soon as there is some wort in the kettle, the hops are added and mixed into the wort. When the kettle is almost full, a fire is again started and the wort is brought to a boil. The wort is then boiled with the hops for an hour, often also for 1.5 hours or even 2 hours for Lagerbier.

Meyer also discusses the amount of hops to use: for Schenkbier or Winterbier, the Bavarian beer price regulation assumes using 15 Pfund (8.4 kg) of hops for 35 Eimer (2394 l) of beer (a hopping rate of 3.5 g/l), while for Lagerbier or Sommerbier, 25 Pfund (14 kg) of hops are assumed to be used to brew 30 Eimer (2052 l) of beer (a hoping rate of 6.8 g/l). To put this into a relationship with the malt to be used, 7 Schäffel (1556 l) of dry malt were meant to be used to brew 49 Eimer (3352 l) of Schenkbier/Winterbier using 21 Pfund (11.76 kg) of hops, or 42 Eimer (2873 l) of Lagerbier/Sommerbier using 35 Pfund (19.6 kg) of hops. For Winterbier/Schenkbier, only old hops are used, while for Sommerbier/Lagerbier, new hops shall be used. Depending on when the beer shall be served, Meyer suggests different hopping rates:

- May and June: 4 Pfund of hops per Schäffel of dry malt
- July and August: at least 5 Pfund of hops per Schäffel of dry malt
- September and October: 6 to 7 Pfund of hops per Schäffel of dry malt

The amount of hops can also be varied depending on the the lagering cellar itself: if it keeps cold even during the hot summer months, the overall amount of hops can be reduced and milder beers can be brewed. But for less than optimal lagering cellars, it is advisable to use more rather than less hops, and to rather brew beer that is a bit too bitter than one that goes sour towards the end of the summer.

After the end of the boil, the wort is scooped through a hop strainer onto a coolship. When the kettle is emptied, water is immediately added to protect it from heat damage.

For the *Nachbier*, the *Oberteig* (top layer of the mash) is first removed, and then hot water is sprinkled on top of the mash. The mash is then mixed through, left to rest for 30 minutes, and then wort for the *Nachbier* is drawn off. It is boiled in a smaller kettle called *Nachbierpfanne* and boiled together with the spent hops from the first beer. After a 30 minute boil, the wort is cooled on a small coolship and then fermented.

Per Schäffel of malt, about 30 to 40 Maß of *Nachbier* can be produced. This beer is usually not sold but rather served to brewers and other service personnel, but can also be used to make vinegar.

After the *Nachbier*, the mash can be treated the same again by sprinkling more water on top of it, mixing it through again, and then drawing off a very thin wort called *Glattwasser*. Together with the *Oberteig*, it can be used in the production of distilled spirits. The spent grains called *Träber* are then removed from the mash tun and used to feed animals or to be sold.

4.2.7 Old Bavarian Method According to Alexander Ziegler (1849)

The brewing process description of Alexander Ziegler [18, pp. 50–57] starts with conditioning and crushing the malt. Taxation in Bavaria at the time was paid per Bavarian Scheffel of conditioned (i.e. slightly wetted) malt, at a rate of 5 Rheinischer Gulden (Rhenish guilder). The dried malt was spread out and water was sprinkled onto it while it kept getting turned over, and then left to rest for 6 hours. The amount of water depended on how old and dry the malt was: freshly kilned malt didn't require as much water as old, dry malt. After the malt had taken up the water, it was expected to increase in volume by about 14 to 16%. In the malt mill, it was then measured and crushed, and the tax was paid on the measurement in the mill. Only then the actual brewing process could start.

Per Bavarian Scheffel of malt, it was expected that about 9 Eimer (615 l) of water would be required, divided up between the mash tun and the kettle. About two thirds of the water went into the mash tun, while the remaining water went into the kettle and was brought to a boil.

The malt was then poured into the mash tun and mixed with the cold water. Then the actual mashing began, which Ziegler describes as an orderly operation controlled through verbal commands. With the order "zusammen in die Mitte" ("together into the centre"), all brewers put their mash paddle towards the middle of the mash tun, pull back the malt from the centre, and with a twist of the mash paddle, push it back towards the centre.

This is synchronised through loud, slow counting (3 times 30). While this mashing is going on, two of the brewers, called *Pfannenknechte* (lit. kettle servants), stop mashing and instead start scooping boiling water from the kettle into the mash tun until it has reached a temperature of 28 °R (35 °C). A bit of hot water is meant to remain in the kettle. The mash is again mixed through thoroughly until the verbal command "auf" orders an end to it. A gutter is then put on top to connect mash tun and kettle, and the brewers start scooping over the first thick mash under the verbal command "scoop only thick", accompanied by singing. This scooping takes about 15 to 25 minutes. Then the mash in the mash tun again gets mixed through and some of the thin mash is drawn off through the false bottom and poured on top.

This first thick mash is then brought to a boil. For Schenkbier, it should boil for 30 minutes, while for Sommerbier, it was usually boiled for 45 minutes. The *Pfannenknecht*'s job is to ensure that it boils just the right amount, neither too little nor too much. In particular, it shouldn't form excessive foam. The author also mentions that the mash should get mixed thoroughly while it heats up and that it should "lift itself up". If the mash doesn't do this properly, he sees this as a fault in how the kettle was built.

After the first thick mash been boiled for the appropriate amount of time, some thin mash is collected through the false bottom to add to the kettle after scooping back. As soon as all brewers are present at the mash tun, the thick mash gets scooped over into the mash tun and stirred in, again synchronised through slow, loud counting (2 times 40). This should increase the mash temperature to 38 °R (47 °C).

Immediately afterwards, the collected wort is added to the kettle, and the second thick mash is scooped over into the kettle, the same way as the first one.

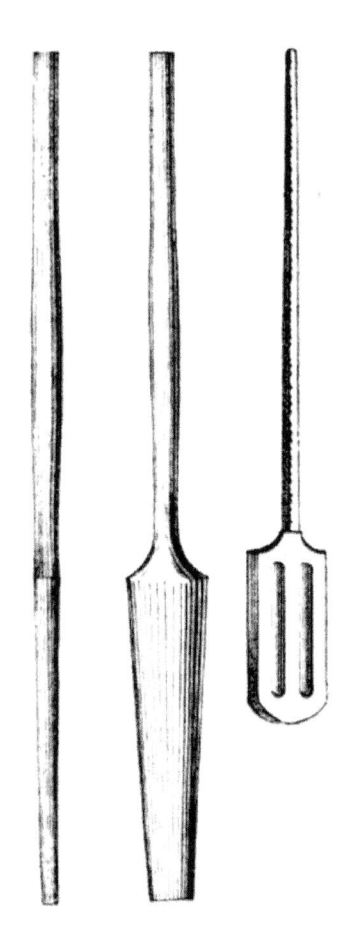

It is again brought to a boil, but is boiled longer than the first one: 45 minutes for Schenkbier and 1 hour for Sommerbier. It is then again scooped back and mixed in, again synchronised through slow, loud counting (4 times 30). The resulting temperature of the mash should then be 48 °R (60 °C).

Then the *Lautermaische*, the thin mash, is scooped over into the kettle, brought to a boil, and boiled for about 15 minutes, until it is mixed back while counting (5 times 30). The resulting temperature should then be 58 to 60 °R (72.5 to 75 °C). The mash is then left to rest for an hour, while the kettle is filled with the *Anschwänzwasser* (sparge water) that is then brought to a boil.

Different constructions of mash paddles [25, p. 123]

After an hour, the valves on the mash tun are opened, and the wort is first poured back onto the mash until it runs clear, and then collected in the *Grand*. The *Anschwänzwasser* is transferred from the kettle to a tub near the mash tun. When the kettle is empty, the wort from the *Grand* is transferred to the kettle. This is called *Aufhacken der Würze* (lit. hacking up the wort). As soon as the kettle's bottom is fully covered with wort, hops are added to the kettle. Wort is drawn off and scooped over until the top of the mash appears in the mash tun.

The *Teig* (the top layer of the mash) is scooped off and used for distilling or animal feed. The valves are then closed, and sparge water at a temperature of 50 to 60 °R (62.5 to 75 °C) is scooped over the mash. After 10 minutes, the valves are opened again, and the clear wort is scooped into the kettle. A fire is then started under the kettle, and the wort is boiled.

Schenkbier is boiled for 1 hours, while Sommerbier is boiled for 1.5 to 2 hours. After this time, flakes of coagulated proteins should be clearly visible and the wort itself should look dark and clear.

The wort is then run through hop strainers made from thin brass wire, and brought onto the coolship, where it is first stirred and then left to cool. This cooling should not take more than 12 hours, but also not be done too quickly. With cool weather, the wort shall cool down to 4 to 8 °R (5 to 10 °C), and is then moved to the fermenters.

From the spent grains in the mash tun, some *Nachbier* or *Schöps* can be brewed by scooping over more water and drawing off some wort. Alternatively, these third runnings are used for distilling. The *Kühlgeläger*, the hot break left on the coolships, can be pressed to get any residual wort out of them, and then also used in the distillery.

The hops that were used depended on the type of beer being brewed. For Schenkbier or Winterbier, simple Landhopfen (country-side hops) was used. For Sommerbier, a larger quantity of hops of a higher quality were used.

Ziegler lists an example of Winterbier brewed from 11.5 Bavarian Scheffel, which would require 30 to 36 Pfund of hops. For Sommerbier made from the same amount of malt, the total amount of hops depended on when the beer was expected to be served.

- May: 38 to 40 Pfund
- June: 42 to 44 Pfund

- July: 46 to 48 Pfund
- August: 50 to 52 Pfund
- September: 54 to 60 Pfund

The hop varieties that Ziegler suggested were Spalter hops and highest quality Saazer hops.

We also get some information on the expected density of malt: according to the author, 11.5 Bavarian Scheffel (2557 l) of malt were equivalent to 26.75 Centner (1498 kg). This means that malt had a density of about 0.585 kg/l.

4.2.8 Old Bavarian or Munich Method According to P. Müller (1854)

In his description of what he calls the "Old Bavarian" or Munich method [3, pp. 254–258], Müller refers to his description of double decoction with two thick mashes that we've explained above. He assumes the production of 36 to 38 Eimer (24.6 to 26 hl) of *Braunbier* from 1320 Pfund (739.2 kg) of malt which he sets at a volume of 6 Scheffel (1334 l), implying a density of 0.554 kg/l of kilned malt. This malt is first lightly wetted and left to stand for 6 hours until it is crushed.

The law in Bavaria at the time mandated that from a Scheffel of malt either 6 Eimer (410 l) of *Lagerbier* or 7 Eimer (478 l) of *Schenkbier* would have to be brewed. Based on this, the total amount of water to be used for brewing was determined. The rule of thumb was that the required amount of water was two times the amount of beer to be brewed. This water was divided up between the mash tun and the brew kettle, with more than a half up to 2/3 going into the mash tun, and less than a half down to 1/3 going into the kettle.

In Müller's example, 50 Eimer (3420 l) of cold water are put into the mash tun, while 34 Eimer (2394 l) of water are brought to a boil in the kettle, which is closer to 60%/40%. The crushed malt is mashed in cold. When the kettle is boiling, the mash gets stirred, and boiling water is slowly added to bring the mash temperature is brought to up to 26 to 28 °R (32.5 to 35 °C). Müller calls this process *Anlauben*. When this temperature is reached and the mash is thoroughly mixed, the first thick mash is scooped over from the mash tun to the kettle so that it contains a total volume of 36 to 37 Eimer (2462 to 2531 l). This is brought to a boil under constant stirring to prevent scorching. After a boil time of 45 minutes, sometimes up to 1.5 hours, the thick mash is scooped back and thoroughly mixed in, to raise the mash temperature to 39 to 40 °R (48.75 to 50 °C).

This is immediately followed by scooping the second thick mash over into the kettle, with a total volume of 38 Eimer (2599 l). Following the same process as with the first thick mash and a total boil time of 45 to 60 minutes, the mash temperature should be at 49 to 50 °R (61.25 to 62.50 °C) after mixing back in the second thick decoction.

This is followed by the *Lautermaische*: thin mash is scooped from the top of the mash tun, to collect 40 to 42 Eimer (2736 to 2873 l) of thin mash in the kettle. It is brought to a boil and boiled for another 15 to 30 minutes. It is then scooped back and mixed in, followed by thorough mashing of 30 more minutes. This process is called *Abmaischen*. The final temperature of the mash shall come in at 58 to 60 °R (72.5 to 75 °C). The mash tun is then covered and left to rest for 1 to 1.5 hours. After this rest, lautering starts, and the wort is collected in the *Grant*. Wort is scooped back into the mash tun until it runs clear.

In the meanwhile, the kettle is completely emptied and cleaned out, filled with any water that would be required for cleaning later as well as for sparging the *Nachbier*, and brought to a boil. The kettle is then again emptied, and the first wort is scooped over into it. A certain quantity of the hops (the original source doesn't mention how much) is then boiled with only some of the wort for 15 to 30 minutes, and only then the rest of the wort is added. The complete wort is then boiled for another 1.5 to 2 hours, after which it is strained through the hop strainer and directed onto the coolship.

Using hot water, called *Anschwänzwasser*, more sugar is extracted from the mash for making *Nachbier*. Per Scheffel of malt, Müller estimates that about 30 to 40 Maß of *Nachbier* can be brewed. This wort can be either collected and also added to the kettle, or it can be boiled separately using the hops from the previous brew, cooled on a separate coolship (*Nachbierkühle*) and fermented separately.

If the *Anschwänzen* (sparging) is continued, any further runnings are called *Glattwasser*, to be used in the production of distilled spirits together with the *Oberteig* and the *Unterteig* as well as other brewery waste.

According to Müller, this brewing method is used relatively consistently across Munich as well as the rest of Old Bavaria (modern Bavaria excluding the regions of Franconia and Swabia).

4.2.9 According to Philipp Heiß (1860)

Philip Heiß was the brewmaster at Gabriel Sedlmayr's Spaten brewery. Naturally, much of his knowledge is based on his experience there, but also on other breweries that he had visited during his brewing career.

Heiß's description of mashing starts off with the brewing water: 1/3 of the total brewing water shall initially be put in the kettle, while 2/3 shall be put into the mash tun. Then the crushed malt is mashed in. All crushed malt is mixed in under constant stirring, and then stirred more until all clumps have disappeared and all the malt has been wetted. Then the cold mash is left to stand for 3 to 4 hours during cold weather, but at most 2 hours during warmer weather.

According to Heiß, any sugar already formed in the malt should get dissolved, so after this initial rest the cold wort should have some natural sweetness. This was seen as a sign for good malt. Then the boiling water from the kettle is moved over to the mash tun so that it can warm the mash and lift it up. This has to happen under constant stirring by all available brewers. After all the water has been added, the resulting temperature of the mash shall be 24 to 28 °R (30 to 35 °C).

Heiß lists a number of special rules for the first thick mash:

1. before the water is scooped over, the fire shall be put to a minimum to prevent damage to the kettle.
2. when scooping over the water, whoever does the scooping shall stop half-way and help mix in for a while, otherwise all the water might get added too quickly.
3. mashing itself needs to be done carefully, in particular all the malt at the bottom of the mash tun, otherwise the temperature will be spread unevenly across the mash.
4. temperature is important: the first thick mash's temperature should not exceed 28 °R (35 °C), but also not go below 25 °R (31.25 °C).
5. before the thick mash is moved to the kettle, the kettle shall be covered sufficiently with thin mash. The fire shall not be increased immediately, but only when the bottom of the kettle has been properly covered, again to prevent damage to the kettle.
6. when all the thick mash is in the kettle, a strong fire shall be stirred up. The thick mash in the kettle needs to be stirred to prevent scorching "until it lifts itself up".
7. after the beginning of the boil, the fire shall be closed enough so that the mash is only slightly boiling.

8. towards the end of the boil, the fire shall be stirred up again so that the mash doesn't fall to the bottom of the kettle when it is mixed back.
9. the mash shall be stirred during mixing back. Before mixing, the mash that had remained in the mash tun shall be dark and clear, while the malt should have sunk to the bottom of the mash tun.
10. while mixing back, the mash shall be stirred constantly until all the boiled mash has been mixed back.

When this is done, this is the point when the first thick mash is back in the mash tun, at an expected temperature of 39 to 41 °R (48.75 to 51.25 °C). Immediately, the bottom of the kettle shall again be covered in thin mash to prevent damage to the kettle. Then the second thick mash is scooped over to the kettle and brought to a boil in the same way as the first thick mash. All the same rules as with the first thick mash shall also be kept.

After the second thick mash has been fully scooped and mixed back into the mash tun, it is then called the lauter mash, at an expected temperature of 48 to 51 °R (60 to 63.75 °C). The kettle needs to be cleaned as thoroughly as possible, and thin mash shall again be used to cover the bottom of the kettle. Then more thin mash is drawn into the *Grand*, from where it is moved to the kettle and brought to a boil. The total volume of thin mash shall be greater than the previous thick mashes. The boil duration of the thin mash depends on the type of beer that is brewed, 15 minutes for Winterbier or Schenkbier, or 30 minutes for Sommerbier or Lagerbier.

This final boil of thin mash shall coagulate the protein, or at least some of it, that is contained in the mash. After the boil time, the thin mash is scooped and mixed back into the main mash and then the whole mash is mashed for another 30 minutes. The final temperature of the mash shall then be at 56 to 60 °R, or 70 to 75 °C. Heiß emphasised that at this stage it is especially important to lift all the malt particles from the bottom of the mash tun up.

After the final mashing, the mash is then left to rest for 1 hour. During this rest, the kettle gets cleaned thoroughly and then its bottom shall be covered with water to prevent damage.

The total time from the first thick mash, i.e. when hot water is mixed into the cold mash to the end of the final rest, shall be 5 hours, and according to Heiß, this time shall be adhered to. Manipulation of the first thick mash including its boil shall take 2 hours, manipulation of the second thick mash including its boil shall take only 1.5 hours, while the final thin mash boil, the final mash and the rest shall take another 1.5 hours.

Then lautering starts by drawing off wort through the false bottom into the *Grand* and carefully scooping it back into the mash so as not stir up the mash, until the wort runs off clear. At this point, the valves are only opened slightly so that the mash doesn't compact from the pressure of the liquid.

After all the wort has run off, the valves are closed, and the top layer of the mash, called *Bierteig*, is removed in many breweries, and sold as animal feed. The mash is then turned over and evened out. Then hot water is added to the mash. This is called *Nachguß* or *Anschwänzen*. This water has been heated up in a second, smaller kettle. This water is then left to rest on the mash for a few minutes, until more wort is drawn off in the same way as before.

The number of runnings that are drawn off and the amount of water used depends on the specific type of beer. With Winterbier or Schenkbier, two *Nachgüße* are done and both runnings are added to the first runnings. With Sommerbier or Lagerbier, two *Nachgüße* are done, but only the second runnings are added to the first runnings, while the third runnings are used to make *Nachbier*.

The quantity of water used also depends on the beer type: in Heiß's example, for a Winterbier brew of 12 Schäffel (2668 l), a total of 70 Brauhausschäffel (897 l) of water are used, divided into 40 Brauhausschäffel (513 l) for the second runnings and 30 Brauhausschäffel (384 l) for the third runnings. For the first *Nachguss* on a Sommerbier brew, 50 Brauhausschäffel (641 l) are used. For the second *Nachguss* that is used for *Nachbier*, another 60 to 70 Brauhausschäffel (769 to 897 l) are poured over the mash.

When enough wort is collected to cover the bottom of the kettle, the prepared hops are added and the fire is stirred to start the boil of what's called the *Hopfenbier* (lit. *hop beer*). The point here is to extract the bitter compounds, tannins, ethereal oils and hop resins as efficiently as possible. The rest of the wort is moved to the kettle, and all the wort is boiled. Sommer- or Lagerbier is boiled for 2 to 2.5 hours, while Winter- or Schenkbier is boiled for only 1 to 1.5 hours.

An iron coolship [26]

After the end of the boil, the wort is then poured through the hop strainer so that only clear wort runs onto the coolship. On the coolship, the wort shall cool as quickly as possible. Heiß saw the temperature range of 18 to 40 °R (22 to 50 °C) as most problematic that needed to be overcome as quickly as possible. The wort itself shall look dark and clear on the coolship, and clear hot break should form. Heiß also mentions that the wort can be beaten or mixed to make it cool quicker, but the forming of foam on the top needs to be avoided, or the foam needs to be removed afterwards. Cooling in total shall take at least 5, but never more than 12 hours, as this would vastly increase the risk of spontaneous, "wild" fermentation. If cooling takes less than 5 hours, not enough hot break would fall out, and the wort wouldn't clear as well.

(Source: [22, pp. 89–107])

4.2.10 Munich Method According to Hermann Pfauth (1870)

The amount of malt and water used to brew beer depends on the type of beer that needs to be brewed. Pfauth distinguishes between normal beer and strong (or luxury) beers. Normal beer types are Sommerbier, also called Lagerbier, and Winterbier, also known as Schenkbier, while typical strong beer types are Salvator, Bockbier and Doppelbier.

According to legal regulation, the amount of malt used for each beer type was predetermined. Given 1 Schäffel of malt, 4 Eimer of Bockbier, 6 Eimer of Sommerbier or 7 Eimer of Winterbier could be brewed. Bockbier would typically have an original gravity of 16 to 17% on the Balling scale, while Sommerbier would have an original gravity of 12.5 to 13% and Winterbier 10.5 to 11.2%. The amount of water is typically about twice the amount of beer that will be brewed.

When brewing beer, the amount of water is initially divided between mashing (two thirds of the total water) and for sparging (one third of the total water) for further extraction from the mash.

The water used for mashing is then split between the mash tun (two thirds) and the kettle (one third). The water in the mash tun is added cold, while the water in the kettle is heated up and brought to a boil later. When this is prepared, the malt is added to the mash tun, and either the mash stirrer is turned on, or the mash is mixed through manually with mash paddles.

The mashing process with a mash paddle consists of two different movements: *Aufmaischen* and *Durchschieben* (lit. *to mash up* and *to push through*). The *Aufmaischen* works by placing the mash paddle in the middle of the mash tun, pulling it to the side of the mash tun and pushing it down to the bottom of the mash tun, then quickly turning the mash paddle and then pulling the handle so that the malt is "thrown" towards the centre. *Durchschieben* on the other hand means placing the mash paddle on the side of the mash tun and continuously pushing the mash along the side of the mash tun so that it gets into a rotating motion inside the mash tun. Both movements are applied alternately, depending on verbal commands from the brewmaster or the lead shift brewer.

As long as crushed malt is still added to the mash, all workers mix in at their own cadence using the *Aufmaischen* movement. When all the crushed malt has been added, the verbal commands "Mitt'" (lit. *middle*) or "z'samm' auf d'Mitt" (lit. *together to the middle*) orders all workers to place their mash paddle in the centre and pull it towards them, followed by the command "Gleich auf" (lit. *equally up*) to turn the mash paddle and push the mash mass towards the middle. This is continued 35 to 40 times, either accompanied by counting 1, 2, 3, … or by singing.

Other verbal commands used are "Fest vom Boden her" (lit. "strong from the ground") to pull the mash paddle not just from the centre, but also from the left and right sides of the worker, "Laßt's brav rauschen" (lit. "let it swoosh well") to throw up the mash harder with the mash paddle, "Durchschieben" or "räumt's aus" (lit. *clear it out*) to start *Durchschieben*, and "Auf" (lit. *up*) or "Hoch auf" (lit. *high up*) to finish mashing.

The cold mash is then left to rest for 3 to 4 hours by some brewers, while most breweries, especially larger ones, immediately begin with the first mash: the mash get thoroughly mixed through while boiling water from the kettle is slowly added to the mash tun until the mash has reached a temperature of 34°C. Mixing continues for another 10 minutes.

Then the first thick mash is moved from the mash tun to the kettle, either by scooping it out or by using a temporary gutter. The amount of thick mash scooped over needs to be of such a volume that, when boiled and mixed back, it increases the mash temperature to 54 °C, but also that about 3 inches of it remain in the kettle to prevent fire damage.

Then the mash valves are briefly opened to loosen any starch in there, to prevent it from blocking any pipes but also to make it available to the mashing process later. If the kettle is located higher than the mash tun, then mash pumps are used to transport the mash into it. When a mash pump is used, the mash paddle is used to push thick mash towards the suction hole if a thick mash is pulled. When a thin mash is pulled (usually for the third decoction), any hard matter is moved to the other side of the mash tun and the suction hole is covered with a brush.

Then the first thick mash in the kettle is brought to a boil. This can take 30 to 45 minutes. During the time when the mash is heating up, it needs to be stirred with a mash paddle to prevent thick bits from settling on the bottom and scorching. Not only would scorched mash change the flavour of the beer, it can also cause damages to the kettle itself. Stirring is only stopped when the mash in the kettle forms a grey layer of foam on the top which means it's close to boiling. When it starts boiling, any light foam that forms on top is beaten back into the mash. Then a bell is rang once that indicates that the actual boil has begun, which lasts 30 minutes for Winterbier, or 45 minutes for Sommerbier. Any foam forming on top is beaten back. If too much foam forms during the boil, the flame needs to be turned down. If no foam forms on top, the flame needs to be turned up.

Five minutes before the thick mash has finished boiling, the bell is rang for a longer time and 2 or 3 tubs of water are prepared to pour into the kettle and to clean its insides. When all workers have arrived, stirring the mash and scooping the first thick mash begins. This is continued until the main mash has reached a temperature of 54°C, the kettle's side are briefly washed with water and the remaining mash in the kettle is stirred through, while mashing in the mash tun continues for another 10 minutes.

When this is finished, the second thick mash is moved to the kettle in the same way as before, this time enough to increase the temperature to eventually reach 65°C. The mash is again brought to a boil, while the mash tun valves are flushed by briefly running off thin mash. The begin of the boil is indicated by ringing the bell twice. The mash is typically boiled the same amount of time as the first time, but some breweries prefer to extend the boil for another 15 minutes. As before, the end of the boil is announced by ringing the bell 5 minutes prior. The mash is again moved back to the mash. If the kettle is completely empty, then mashing is stopped briefly to scoop thin mash back into it. When enough thin mash been transferred, mixing the main mash also stops and the mash tun valves are again briefly flushed. The amount of thin mash must be sufficient for bringing the mash temperature to 73 to 75 °C when mixing it back after boiling it.

The thin mash is then brought to a boil. Unlike the two previous mashes, it doesn't require any mixing as it ideally shouldn't contain any hard matter that could scorch at the bottom. Ringing the bell 3 times indicates that the boil has started, which lasts 15 minutes for Winterbier and 30 minutes for Sommerbier. After the boil, the thin mash is scooped back in the main mash and thoroughly mixed in to reach around 74°C. After this, mashing continues for another 30 minutes.

Meanwhile, the kettle is cleaned out with water. Some water is kept in the kettle to prevent fire damage. Then the mash tun valves are slowly opened to draw off some wort which is carefully scooped back on top of the mash. After this, the mash is left to rest for 30 to 60 minutes.

After this rest, the whole mash is again stirred through and wort is drawn off from the mash tun valves and poured back into the mash until it runs clear. Then the mash tun valves are opened more to fill the *Grand* with wort. When it is three quarters full, the water in the kettle is removed and the wort from the *Grand* is transferred to it instead. As soon as the kettle is filled with 3 to 4 inches of wort, hops are added.

For Winterbier, 2 to 2.5 Pfund of medium quality hops such as Hallertauer are added per Schäffel of malt used. For Sommerbier, the planned position in the lagering cellar has an impact on the hopping rate:

- Beer that will be served in May or June receives 2.5 Pfund of medium quality hops per Schäffel of malt.
- Beer served in July and August will be hopped with 3 Pfund of fine quality hops such as Saazer or Spalter hops per Schäffel of malt.
- Beer served in September and October receives 4 Pfund fine quality hops per Schäffel of malt.

When all wort has been drawn off, the grey, slimy top layer on the mash is removed, to be used as animal feed or in distilling. After that, hot water is poured on top of the mash, called *Anschwänzen*, which (as mentioned earlier) should be one third of the total brew water, divided into 2 to 3 portions. Using cold water in this process would not only mean that the malt will be insufficiently extracted, it can also bring down the mash temperature to ranges that are ideal for the formation of lactic acid.

Alternatively, the first pour of *Anschwänzen* can also be done while there is still a liquid on top of the mash. In that case, a wooden board is put on top of the mash, and the first amount of water is poured on top of the board. Since the wort has a higher specific gravity, it shouldn't mix with the water during this process, and thus the water simply "follows" the wort when it is drawn off. All wort gained that way should immediately be moved to the kettle. The final runnings should have a specific gravity of 3% on the Balling scale.

After this, more cold water is poured on top of the mash and drawn off (called *Glattwasser*), which is later used in distilling. The spent grains are used as animal feed.

When all the wort has been collected in the kettle, it is brought to a boil. When the wort starts boiling, the bell is rung 4 times. The length of the wort boil depends on certain factors, for some brewers when hot break becomes visible in the wort, for others when a certain original gravity on the Balling scale has been reached. For Winterbier, the boil time is typically 60 to 90 minutes, for Sommerbier 2 hours, and for stronger beers such as Bockbier 3 to 4 hours. During the first half of the boil, it shall be vigorous, while for the second half, it shall only lightly boil to promote the formation of big clumps of hot break in the wort.

When the wort boil has finished, the wort is then pumped from the kettle through a wort strainer onto a coolship. This is again indicated by prolonged ringing of the bell. The let the wort cool faster, it is sometimes stirred with dedicated paddles or water-cooled through a system of tubes. The stirring of the wort also has the purpose to oxygenate the wort to precipitate more proteins. When the wort has reached 20 to 23°C, it is left to rest so that any *Trub* can precipitate and settle on the bottom of the coolship. Typically, wort should be left on the coolship for at least 5 hours, but at the same time not more than 12 hours, as that would increase the danger of the wort souring during warmer weather. The temperature range for the wort to be moved to the fermenters should be between 4 and 10°C, ideally 5 to 6°C.

(Source: [23, pp. 96–122])

4.2.11 Munich or Bavarian Method According to Carl Lintner (1878)

The amount of water used to brew depends on the type of beer, in particular whether *Lagerbier* or *Schenkbier* is brewed. Taking

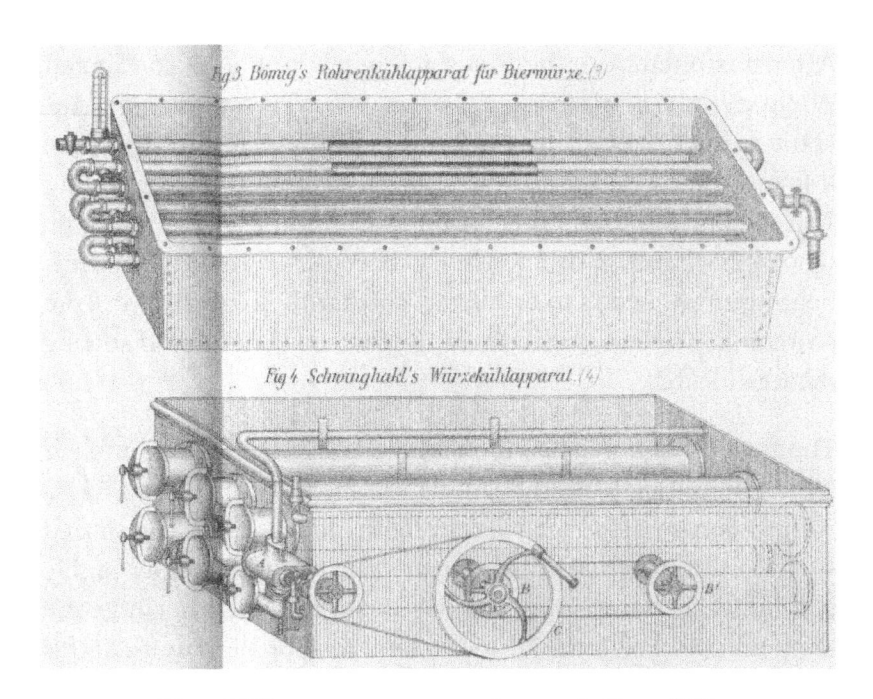

Two 1870s constructions of wort chillers [27]

evaporation, the wort left behind in the spent grains, the hops and the settled cold break on the coolship into account, on average nearly twice the amount of water is required compared to the amount of wort produced. On average, from one Hektoliter of malt (equivalent to 103 Zollpfund, i.e. 51.5 kg), 1.85 to 2.13 Hektoliter of beer are produced.

The water is divided up so that about 2/3 are used for mashing and 1/3 are used as *Nachguss*, i.e. as water for sparging. Of the water intended for mashing, about 140 litres of water at ambient temperature are used for mashing in 1 Zentner of malt (= 50 kg), while the remaining water is brought to a boil in the kettle.

According to Lintner, this initial mash would then be left to rest for 2 hours during warm weather, or 3 to 4 hours during cold weather, but in the 1870s, it was already common to bring the mash up to a temperature of 34 to 35 °C by mixing in boiling water.

After this operation, the first thick mash boiling is conducted. While vigorously mashing, 1/3 of its volume is transferred to the kettle as thick mash. Then the kettle gets heated up slowly so that it takes at least 30 minutes for the thick mash to begin boiling. The thick mash then boils for 30 to 45 minutes, depending on whether *Schenkbier* or *Lagerbier* is brewed. When the mash is heating up, it needs to be stirred constantly to prevent it from scorching. Modern breweries of the time used dedicated stirring devices for this.

The boiled thick mash is then mixed back into the main mash, which should increase the temperature to between 50 and 54 °C. Almost immediately, again a third of the total mash is transferred to the kettle and treated like the first thick mash. Lintner highly recommends dampening the fire when the thick mash is at a temperature of 63 to 65 °C and to let it rest for 30 minutes at this temperature before it is brought to a full boil.

After boiling the second thick mash, it is again mixed back, which should raise the main mash's temperature to 63 to 65 °C. Then, this mash is drawn off, moved to the kettle in such a quantity that it will increase the temperature of the mash to 72 to 75 °C. After boiling the thin mash for 20 to 30 minutes, it is mixed back into the main mash.

When the final saccharification temperature is reached, the mash is left to rest for 30 to 60 minutes, and only then, lautering begins.

In total, the whole process from mashing in until mashing out should last about 4 to 5 hours and effect a complete conversion of the malt.

When all of the wort is drawn off, the *Oberteig*, a grey, slimy mass on top of the mash, is removed and often used as animal feed. Quite often, it is also mixed into the mash when it gets hacked up. Then sparging commences, where the remaining 1/3 of the water that has been heated up is sprinkled on top of the mash in

2 to 3 portions. This is called *Anschwänzen*. Some breweries at the time already used dedicated sparging devices called *schottisches Drehkreuz* (lit. *Scottish turnstile*).

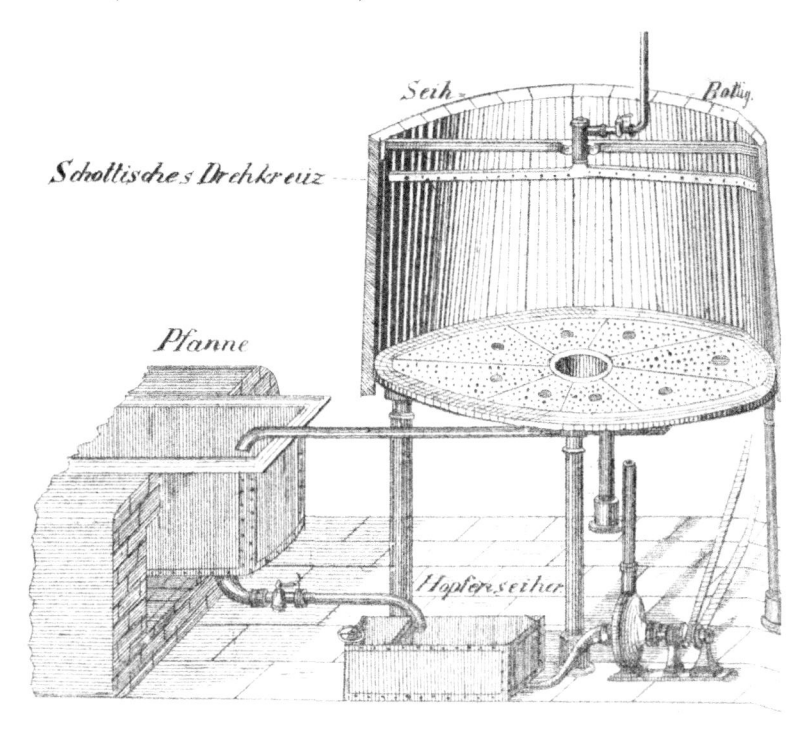

A combined system of lauter tun (*Seih-Bottig*) with integrated sparge arm (*Schottisches Drehkreuz*), kettle (*Pfanne*) and hop strainer (*Hopfenseiher*) [23, p. 236]

Another method of sparging is to put a wooden board on top of the mash and to slowly pour some of the sparging water on top of it so that the water level remains the same. Due to different specific gravities of wort and added water, stratification can be expected, and the water will rinse out the grain when it is running through the mash. The remaining sparge water is then poured over the mash after it's been hacked up.

All the wort is collected in the kettle. The last runnings should have an extract of about 3° Balling. When all the wort is in the kettle, it is brought to a boil so that it can boil together with the hops.

The amount of hops depends on the type of beer that is brewed and when it is brewed. For *Winterbier*, about 620 grams of hops are estimated for 50 kg of malt. For *Sommerbier*, the amount of hops depend on when the beer shall be served: beer brewed for May and June shall be brewed with 750 grams of hops, beer for July and August with 870 grams of hops, and beer for September and October with 990 grams of hops.

The overall time of boiling depends on both when sufficient hot break is achieved as well as the amount of extract concentration the beer shall reach. For *Winterbier*, this can be 60 to 90 minutes, for *Sommerbier*, this would be typically 2 hours, while for even stronger beers, the wort can boil for 3 to 4 hours. The first half of the boil shall be vigorous, while the second half should be less strong to help with the formation and clumping of hot break.

In total, one brew takes about 9 hours.

(Source: [20, pp. 241–243])

4.2.12 Old Bavarian Method According to Franz Cassian (1887)

At the time of writing, this method was considered to be old-fashioned and only used in breweries with inadequate equipment. Mashing and lautering was done in the same vessel that therefore also had to be equipped with a false bottom. Typically, no automated stirrers were installed, and water would typically be added through a pipe installed on the side of the mash tun, called *Pfaff*, to add water from underneath the false bottom, akin to underletting. Underneath the mash tun, a *Grand* was installed, a vessel in which the lautered wort was collected. Ideally, it would have been big enough to contain all the collected wort.

The brewing process itself worked like this: the ratio of water to malt was 8 parts water to 1 part of malt by weight. One third of the water is added to the mash tun and optionally warmed through steam if it's especially cold, the remaining two thirds are added to the kettle and brought to a boil.

Mashing in the crushed malt into the cold water was done three to four hours before the water in the kettle started boiling. This was done because mashing in was slow, manual work as no pre-mashers or other automated mash stirrers existed. When the water was boiling, it was very slowly added to the mash and mixed in. If this was done too quickly, the malt could get scalded, i.e. the diastatic power could get deactivated through high temperatures. The resulting mash temperature should then be 37 to 38 °C. This of course requires a very slow rate at which hot water is added to the mash.

As soon as the final mash temperature has been reached, one third of the mash, in particular the thick portion of it, was scooped into the kettle and brought to a boil as quickly as possible. While bringing the mash up to temperature, it had to be stirred constantly so as to prevent it from scorching on the side of the kettle. The first thick mash was boiled for half an hour and then the boiled mash was pumped back into the main mash under constant stirring. The resulting mash temperature should be 45 to 50 °C. At this stage, the mash should start liquifying fairly quickly as the diastase starts working. During this period, the mash shall be stirred for 15 minutes until the second thick mash is boiled.

The second thick mash is again scooped out from main mash into the kettle. As before, about a third of the total volume is moved over, and mostly the thick portion should be scooped into the kettle. It is again brought to a boil and boiled for 15 minutes. Afterwards it is again mixed back to bring the mash up to a temperature of 60 to 63 °C. After mixing through the mash for 15 minutes, again one third of the mash, this time the thin portion, is moved to the kettle and again brought to a boil and boiled for 15 minutes. After mixing back the hot liquid into the mash tun, the final mash temperature shall be at 73 to 75 °C.

At this stage, boiling is finished, but not the mashing process itself: the mash is mixed through until the malt is quickly sinking to the bottom of the vessel. The mash is then left to rest until all the malt has settled at the bottom. This is when lautering is started. The wort that is drawn off is scooped back onto the mash until it runs clear. The wort then runs off into the *Grand* from where it is pumped into the kettle.

The mash is then sparged by sprinkling hot water on top of it. For strong beers, about 30 litres of water are used for every 100 kg of malt. For weaker beers, 60 litres of water are used. The collected second runnings are added to the first runnings.

The second sparge is done with 50 to 60 litres. This wort collected from it is processed separately to make a weaker beer called *Schöps*. The third sparge with 30 to 40 litres results in *Glattwasser* which is used for distillation.

(Source: [28, pp. 253–256])

4.2.13 New Munich Method According to Franz Cassian (1887)

While Franz Cassian considered the method described in the previous section as entirely obsolete and only used in small countryside breweries, he discussed the methods used in 1880's Munich as state of the art: the brew systems were driven by steam engines, mash tun and lauter tun were separate vessels, and brew systems were not equipped with a *Grand* in the traditional sense.

Mashing in was done using pre-mashing apparatuses and strong, steam-powered stirrers. Hot water was added from a hot liquor tank to effortlessly reach the required temperatures. All mashes were boiled to exact amounts of time, and pumps were used to automate moving mash and wort between brewing vessels.

Due to this automation, the overall brewing process was completed quicker than through the manual brewing process, and specific amounts of finished mash could be continuously produced a narrowly defined amount of time.

The new Munich method still used two thick mash boils and one thin mash boil. The amount of water and malt were generally the same as with the old method, but more recently, the use of saccharometers had become more prevalent and the amount of malt and water was determined using the experience gained with it.

First, the malt was mixed with water using a pre-mashing apparatus. Then hot water is added to bring the mash temperature up to 30 °C. All stirring is automated. The first thick mash is drawn off, boiled for 15 to 45 minutes and then mixed back to bring the mash temperature up to 30 °C (please note that this temperature is probably wrong in the original source). The second thick mash is then drawn off, boiled for the same length of time, and mixed back to bring the mash temperature to 65 °C. The thin mash is then drawn off, again boiled for the same length of time, and again mixed back to bring the final mash temperature up to 75 °C.

Then lautering begins and the mash is sparged. The total amount of water used for sparging is 2/3 of the amount of water used for mashing in.

(Source: [28, pp. 256–259])

4.3 Brewing Method in Nuremberg and Augsburg

4.3.1 Method of Brewing at Augsburg According to David Booth (1834)

In Augsburg, both kettle and mash tuns are of a square form. The false bottom is made of wood. 16.5 barrels (2700 litres) of beer are brewed from 4.85 quarters (1411 litres) of malt and 42.4 pounds (19.23 kg) of hops. The malt is ground extremely fine. As a filtering aid, the spent hops from a previous brew are first spread over the false bottom, then the dry malt is put on top. Five barrels (818 litres) of water are then put on top. This is left to hydrate for six hours, then the cold wort is drawn off, which should be about half a barrel (82 litres). The wet malt is then loosened and turned with a shovel.

The water in the kettle is brought up to a "sufficient heat" (the original text mentions no specific temperature) and is then under-let to the malt just so that it reaches the level of the malt in the mash tun. It is then mashed for 30 minutes, and more hot water is under-let to raise the mash temperature to 60 °C. The cold wort collected earlier is added to the remaining water in the kettle, as well as any more cloudy wort drawn off from the mash tun until it runs clear.

The mash is now left to rest for 2 hours, after which wort is drawn off and pumped into the coolers, where it gets constantly stirred by the means of rakes. In the meantime, the liquid in the kettle is brought to a boil, and 3/4 of it is added to the mash and mashed for 30 minutes, reaching a temperature of 67 °C.

Then the complete mash is moved to the kettle where it boils for 45 minutes. It is then returned to the mash tun, where it is roused until it reaches a temperature of 86 °C. The mash tun is now allowed to settle. During this time, the cold wort from the coolers is pumped into the kettle, and the hops are added. Then the wort from the mash tun is also drawn off and pumped into the kettle. The kettle is then brought to a boil and boils for a total of 2 hours. During this time, a cold mash is done with the remaining mash, the resulting wort is used in the next brew.

When the wort has finished boiling, it is pumped into the coolers, and left to cool until it is at about 7°C. Then six gallons (27 litres) of yeast are added, and the wort is moved to fermenters that hold about 12 barrels (1963 litres) each. After about 7 days, the beer should be clear and is then moved into large vats, with about two inches between the head and the surface of the beer. The beer undergoes a small secondary fermentation, and after 3 to 6 weeks, the vats are bunged up. The beer is ready to drink after 2 months, but is generally kept in vats for 12 to 18 months, when it is drawn off into small serving casks and sent to customers.

One technique particular to Augsburg is that the store vats are coated on the inside with pitch, but instead of letting the pitch cool, the beer is added when the pitch is still hot, thus imparting a peculiar flavour which distinguishes Augsburg beer from the rest of Bavaria.

(Source: [24, p. 29])

4.3.2 According to J.C. Leuchs (1839)

Both Schenkbier and Lagerbier are brewed "auf Satz" in Nuremberg, as this method has turned out to work better to produce mild beers using the local water with a salt content of 0.25 to 0.5%, compared to other brewing methods.

The malt is conditioned 36 hours before it is crushed, first with 6 Maß of water per Bavarian Scheffel of malt, and 18 to 20 hours later with another 2 Maß of water per Scheffel.

The total amount of water needed to brew Schenkbier is 12 Eimer per Scheffel of malt, for Lagerbier 11 Eimer per Scheffel. Two thirds minus a few Eimer go into the kettle, while a third goes into the mash tun. Of the water meant for the mash, initially two thirds go into the mash tun. Then the crushed malt is added on top of the water, and then the remaining water is added on top of the crushed malt. This is then rested for 4 hours without stirring the malt and the water.

Then the cold liquid (called "kalter Satz") is drawn off almost completely from the mash, and kept in the Grant underneath the mash tun. When the water in the kettle has been boiled for 45 to 60 minutes, first mashing commences. For this, hot water from the kettle is poured over the cold mash and thoroughly mixed through until the mash has reached a temperature of 47.5 to 50°C. The hot water is added through a Pfaffe so as to underlet the mash. This first mash takes a total of 45 to 60 minutes. When adding the water to the mash is finished, the "kalter Satz" kept in the Grant is added to the remaining hot water in the kettle.

After some rest, the liquid in the mash is again carefully drawn off as clear as possible and is added to a separate coolship to cool it off as quickly as possible. This is called "warmer Satz". How much "warmer Satz" is collected depends on the weather as well as on the beer type. With cool weather, for every Scheffel of malt, about 1 to 1.5 Eimer of "warmer Satz" are drawn off when Schenkbier is brewed, less when Lagerbier is brewed.

When enough "warmer Satz" has been collected, the remaining wort is drawn off so that only a little bit of liquid is left back in the mash. This wort is also added to the kettle, which is then briefly brought to a boil to then commence the second mash.

For that, the liquid in the kettle is added to the mash via the Pfaff and the mash is thoroughly mixed through. Enough liquid is added until the mash has reached a temperature of 60 to 62.5°C. Only a small amount of liquid should be left in the kettle. Then the complete mash is slowly scooped from the mash tun into the kettle so that the mash tun's false bottom should become visible. This should take about 45 to 60 minutes and should not be rushed.

The mash is then brought to a boil and boiled for 45 to 60 minutes if Schenkbier is brewed, or 75 to 90 minutes if Lagerbier is brewed. While the mash is brought to a boil, it needs to be stirred constantly so as not to scorch. This heating up process should also be slow, at least 30 minutes before boiling begins. This is meant to give the mash time to convert some of the starches into fermentable and unfermentable sugars. When the boil is finished, the mash is scooped back into the mash tun. Then the third mash commences. For that, the whole mash is thoroughly mixed through for at least 45 to 60 minutes, and should eventually end up at a temperature of 72.5 to 75°C.

The kettle is then cleaned out with a small amount of wort kept back in the Grant, or ideally with clean water. Then the "warmer Satz" is added from the coolship to the kettle. The required amount of hops are added to the kettle, and the wort in the kettle should warm up to about 25°C from the residual heat of the coal embers underneath the kettle. This is meant to help with extraction of the hop oils and to bind them to prevent them from evaporating.

The amount of hops depends on the quality of the hops as well as the strength of the beer and how long the beer is meant to be kept. For Schenkbier, a mix of two thirds old hops and one third hops from the most recent harvest are used, at an amount of about 3 Pfund of hops for every Scheffel of malt being used for brewing. For Lagerbier, only recent hops are used, for the earlier batches of the brewing season at an amount of about 4 Pfund per Scheffel, for late season batches 5 to 6 Pfund per Scheffel. Early batches are expected to be served around May, while late batches are usually served in the months of September to November.

After a rest of 30 minutes, drawing off the wort begins. It is added to the kettle to slowly mix it with the hops already in the kettle. When half of the kettle is filled, it can be brought to a boil while more wort is drawn off and added. The wort is then boiled, for Schenkbier this takes about 60 to 90 minutes, while for Lagerbier, the wort is boiled for 2 to 3 hours.

When the wort is drawn off, the top layer of the mash is removed and cold water is added to draw off second runnings. These can be either added to the kettle or used to brew a separate *Nachbier*. Using more cold water, third runnings are drawn off which find their use in distillation.

After the boil, the wort is separated from the hops and cooled on coolships down to 25°C while being stirred, and then another 5 to 6 hours to let it cool completely, ideally to 6.25 to 7.5°C, but sometimes due to the weather, it can only be cooled to 13.75°C before it is moved to the fermenters. Wort that doesn't run off clear from the coolships is run through a filtering cloth.

(Source: [15, pp. 14–24])

4.3.3 According to A. Herrmann (1839)

To brew a batch of beer, the water needed for 1 Schäffel (222 l) of malt amounts to 12 Eimer (820 l) for Schenkbier and 11 Eimer (752 l) for Lagerbier. Of this water, slightly less than two thirds are put in the kettle, while the rest is put in the mash tun. Initially, only two thirds of the mash tun water is added. Then the crushed malt is evenly spread in the mash tun, and then the remaining one third of the mash tun water is poured on top of it. This is left to rest for 4 hours without mixing it through.

After this rest, the thin mash, called *kalter Satz*, is drawn off, and the mash is worked through with shovels to ensure that no dry malt is in the mash anymore. The *kalter Satz* remains in the *Grand*.

When the water in the kettle has boiled for 45 to 60 minutes, the first mash begins: hot water from the kettle is scooped onto the mash while thoroughly getting mixed through, until the mash reaches a temperature of 38 to 40 °R (47.5 to 50 °C). This first mashing is done for 45 to 60 minutes in total. The *kalter Satz* is then moved into the kettle together with the remaining hot water.

After some rest, wort is drawn off from the mash and put onto a dedicated coolship to let it cool. This wort is called *warmer Satz*. The amount of *warmer Satz* getting collected depends on the season, the weather and the type of beer being brewed. During cool weather, about 1 to 1.5 Eimer (68 to 102 l) of *warmer Satz* are collected per Schäffel of malt when brewing Schenkbier, less wort is collected for Lagerbier. This *warmer Satz* remains on the coolship for now.

The remaining wort is then drawn off from the mash and scooped into the kettle to combine it with the *kalter Satz*. The kettle is then briefly brought to a boil, and then scooped back into the mash tun and thoroughly mixed in until the mash has reached a temperature of 48 to 50 °R (60 to 62.5 °C).

Then, the complete mash is scooped back into the kettle so that the false bottom of the mash tun is visible. Scooping over this *Dickmaisch* is done over the course of 45 to 60 minutes. The mash is then brought to a boil and boiled for a considerable amount of time, 45 to 60 minutes for Schenkbier, and 75 to 90 minutes for Lagerbier. Before the mash is fully boiling, it needs to be stirred to prevent scorching.

The thick mash is then scooped back into the mash tun. During this time, it needs to be mashed through in the kettle so that the malt doesn't all sink to the bottom which would make the scooping harder. The mash is then left to cool to between 58 and 60 °R (72.5 to 75 °C). The kettle is then cleaned with some wort or water which is also scooped into the mash tun.

The *warmer Satz* that was kept on the coolship is then added to the kettle, and hops are added to it. The fire under the kettle is then stirred and the wort is heated up to 50 to 60 °R (62.5 to 75 °C) over the course of 2 to 3 hours. The wort is then drawn off from the mash and added to the kettle, which is then brought to a boil. The wort is then boiled for 60 to 90 minutes if Schenkbier is brewed, or 2 to 3 hours if Lagerbier is brewed.

When the mash tun is emptied, the top layer (*Oberteig*) is removed and cold water is poured over the mash to collect more wort. The amount of water used shall be about 1 Eimer (68 l) per Schäffel (222 l) of malt. These second runnings are either added to the already boiling wort or sometimes also used to brew a *Nachbier*.

(Source: [13, pp. 47–53])

4.3.4 Brewing "auf Satz" or Augsburg Method According to Friedrich Meyer (1847)

The "Brauen auf Satz" method is also called the Augsburg brewing method as it was mainly used by breweries in and around the city. It was also used in Nuremberg, but with some deviations in the process itself. Some breweries conduct 4 mashes, where they start at a mash-in temperature of 40 to 42 °C and end with a thin "lauter" mash, while other breweries skip the fourth thin "lauter" mash and start at a mash-in temperature of 50°C. Despite introducing it as the Augsburg Method, the author describes mashing it was conducted in Nuremberg.

The process starts with adding a certain quantity of water to the mash tun. For *Schenkbier* or *Winterbier*, 14 *Eimer* of water needed to be used per *Schäffel* of conditioned, crushed malt, while for *Lagerbier* or *Sommerbier*, only 13 *Eimer* were needed for the same amount of malt. This water is first filled into the kettle, and any remaining water is added to the mash tun. To get the correct amount of water into both vessels, a marked stick should be used to measure the exact volume. The crushed malt is then added to the mash tun, but only spread out and not mixed in. It is left like that for 4 hours, during which the water in the kettle is brought to a boil.

After four hours, 4 to 5 Eimer of liquid are drawn from the mash tun into the Grand, a vessel just below the mash tun tap. This liquid is called "kalter Satz" and will later be added to the kettle. After the "kalter Satz" has been removed, a shovel is used to work the mash so that all clumps of malt are broken up and no dry malt remains.

When the water has come to a boil and the "kalter Satz" has been removed, the boiling water is scooped from the kettle into the mash tun through a *Pfaffe* and mixed into the mash, which means essentially a form of underletting. Transferring boiling water to the mash tun continues until the mash has reached a temperature of 50°C. When this point is reached, no more water is transferred, but the mashing continues for a while. The collected "kalter Satz" is added to the remaining hot water in the kettle. The mash is then left to rest for 15 minutes.

After this rest, liquid is again drawn from the mash tun. The quantity of liquid drawn shall be equal to the amount of hot water that was previously added to the mash. This liquid is added to the kettle which is brought to a boil. The liquid needs to be drawn quickly to ensure that it draws out some of the dissolved components of the malt itself. When the kettle is full, the mash tun tap is closed and the mash is left to rest for another 15 minutes, while the Grand gets completely cleaned.

After this short rest, the mash tun tap is opened again, and so much liquid is drawn off so that for every Schäffel of malt used in the brew, 1.5 Eimer of liquid are collected, i.e. for a brew of 8 Schäffel of malt, 12 Eimer of liquid need to be drawn off. This liquid should be very sweet and totally clear. It is called "warmer Satz". It is immediately added to a small coolship which needs to be placed in such a way that the liquid can be easily added to the kettle later on.

As soon as the liquid in the kettle has come to a boil, second mashing commences, where the boiling liquid is mixed back into the mash and is thoroughly mashed through. Again, the hot liquid is added through the *Pfaffe*. Adding liquid to the mash is stopped when it has reached a temperature of 62°C. Ideally, all of the liquid in the kettle is used, so if any remains, it is kept there to be united with the next mash added to it. After the temperature of 62°C has been reached, the complete mash is added to the kettle, except for the "warmer Satz" in the coolship. The kettle is then immediately brought to a boil, and boiled for an hour if Schenkbier is brewed, or 1.5 hours if Lagerbier is brewed. Typically, the mash is transferred to the kettle through a removable gutter that connects mash tun and kettle into which the mash is scooped. To make scooping easier, the mash needs to be constantly kept in motion to prevent anything from sinking to the bottom.

After the mash has been boiled, it is transferred back into the mash tun and then mashed through further for up to an hour. It is then left to rest for 30 minutes up to 2 hours, depending on the brewery. In the meanwhile, the kettle gets cleaned and the "warmer Satz" is transferred into the kettle, ensuring that none of the sediment in the coolship makes it to the kettle. Hops are then added to the kettle and mixed in and left to stand without heating up the kettle.

In terms of hops, 15 Pfund of hops should be used per 35 Eimer of *Winterbier* or *Schenkbier*, while for *Lagerbier*, 25 Pfund of hops should be used per 30 Eimer. *Winterbier* or *Schenkbier* that is consumed 4 to 6 weeks after brewing, only old hops are used at a rate of 3 Pfund per Schäffel of malt. For *Sommerbier* or *Lagerbier*, only new hops should be used, while the amount of hops can also vary depending on when the beer will be served: May and June, 4 Pfund of hops per Schäffel of dry malt, July and August, at least 5 Pfund of hops, while for September and October, 6 to 7

Pfund of the best new hops, so that for the last beer served, 1 to 1.062 Pfund per Eimer of beer are added.

The amount of hops used also depends on the conditions of the lagering cellar. In a good, cold cellar, less hops can be used which makes for a milder beer, while under sub-optimal conditions, it is better to add too many hops rather than too little, as the hops are crucial for the beer's stability, and it is better for the beer to be bitter than it going sour. The ideal temperature of a good cellar is never above 6 to 7.5°C, even during the hottest days of summer.

After the rest, the mash tun valves are opened and the wort is drawn off and added to the kettle. The wort is then boiled for 1.5 hours for Schenkbier or 2 hours for Lagerbier, then scooped to the coolship, cooled and then fermented and lagered.

(Source: [11, pp. 189–195])

4.3.5 Augsburger and Nuremberg Beer, According to Philipp Heiß (1860)

The brewing process begins in the evening at 8pm. The crushed malt is added dry to the mash tun, then a quarter of the complete amount of brewing water is added on top. To ensure that the water spreads evenly all over the malt, planks of wood are put on top of it. That way, the malt and the water and left to rest for 3 hours. Then the valves are slowly opened, and the "kalter Satz" is slowly run off, which can take 4 to 5 hours on a brew system sized at 10 to 12 Schäffel. Naturally, the mash tun is equipped with a false bottom.

In the kettle, the remaining three quarters of the brewing water are brought to a boil. Ideally, it should start boiling at 4am when the "kalter Satz" has been fully run off. The mostly dry malt is then turned over using a shovel, then the boiling water is added through a *Pfaff* to lift the malt. While hot water is being added, the mash is getting thoroughly mixed through. Water is added until the mash has reached a temperature of 52 to 56 °C, while the mash gets mixed through for a little longer.

After that, the *kalter Satz*, which has been kept in the *Biergrand*, is added to the remaining hot water in the kettle. Then the valves of the mash tun are fully opened to run off all the liquid in the mash into the *Grand*. Then the valves get closed again, and this *Läutermaische* is also added to the kettle.

After 30 minutes rest, more liquid can be collected in the *Grand* by opening the mash tun valves again, but this time slowly, i.e. over the course of 2 hours. This liquid should be very clear and is put in a separate coolship to cool it down. This is called "warmer Satz".

While the "warmer Satz* is run off, the liquid in the kettle is brought to a boil. A thick layer of foam should form on top which needs to be skimmed off. When the liquid is boiling, it is scooped over the mash and thoroughly mixed through. This should bring the mash temperature up to 67 to 70°C.

Then the complete mash is scooped back into the kettle, brought to a boil and boiled for 45 to 60 minutes. After the mash has been boiled, it is scooped back into the mash tun. It should eventually reach a temperature of 82 to 87°C. During this time, the kettle gets cleaned, then the "warmer Satz" is added from the coolship to the kettle, and the hops are added as well. The quantity of hops used per Schäffel of malt are 2.5 to 3 Pfund for Winterbier, and 3 to 5 Pfund for Sommerbier. Then lautering begins and the collected wort is immediately added to the kettle as well.

(Source: [22, pp. 145–146])

4.3.6 Satzverfahren According to Carl Lintner (1878)

This method was prominent in Augsburg and Nuremberg, but by the 1870s, was hardly employed anymore there due the large amount of time and labour that went into this practice.

The mash tun is equipped with a *Pfaff*, a tube that allows underletting, i.e. adding water from underneath the mash tun's false bottom.

For 100 parts of malt, 300 to 320 parts of cold water are used to mash in, either by adding the malt to the water in the mash tun, or by adding the malt to the empty mash tun, adding a flat strainer on top, and pouring the water on top of it.

After a rest of 2 to 4 hours, the liquid, called *kalter Satz*, is drawn off and collected in a vessel called *Grand*, which can take several hours. The remaining water is brought to a boil, the mash is hacked up and mixed through, and the boiling water is mixed in while the mash is stirred vigorously. This is done until the mash temperature has reached 52 to 56 °C. The water is then stopped but mashing continues for another 10 minutes. Then the *kalter Satz* is added to the remaining water in the kettle.

After that, the tap on the mash tun is opened wide and the cloudy wort is drawn off and added to the kettle, which is then slowly brought to a boil. Sometimes, the mash is stirred to produce a wort particularly rich in starches. When the wort starts running clear, the tap is closed. After an hour, the tap is opened again and clear wort is collected in an amount that is roughly equivalent to the weight of the malt used in brewing. This wort is called *warmer Satz* and is brought onto the coolship. Any further wort that is run off is added to the kettle.

When the wort in the kettle has started boiling, it is added back to the mash tun and thoroughly mashed through, which should raise the mash temperature to 72 to 75 °C.

Now a large amount of the mash is scooped over to the kettle and brought to a boil. A small amount of mash needs to remain to aid in full saccharification later as boiling the mash will denature the required enzymes in the boiled mash. Lintner does not say what amount needs to be held back, but rather says this is something to be answered by practical experience. The thick mash is then boiled for 45 to 60 minutes, scooped back into the mash tun and mashed through which should increase the mash temperature to between 82 and 87 °C.

The kettle gets cleaned, the *warmer Satz* is added together with the hops, and then the wort from the mash tun is drawn off and added to the kettle as well.

(Source: [20, pp. 247–249])

4.3.7 Augsburg Method According to Franz Cassian (1887)

Franz Cassian calls this method both Augsburg Method and "auf Satz brauen". It starts with mashing in the malt cold. For brewing Sommerbier, 600 litres of water are used for 100 kg of malt, while for Winterbier, 700 litres of water are needed for the same amount of malt. The water is divided up between the mash tun and the kettle in a certain ratio that is not mentioned by the author. Before doughing in, the false bottom is sprinkled with hops, mainly for the reason to prevent lactic acid fermentation during mashing.

The cold mash should be very thin and is left to rest for 4 to 5 hours. After this time, wort is drawn off through the false bottom into the *Grand*. This malt extract is called *kalter Satz*. The water in the kettle is then brought to a boil. A few litres of *kalter Satz* are added to the boiling water. The boiling water is then underlet into the mash tun which needs to be mixed through so that the boiling water can properly penetrate it. After that, the *kalter Satz* is pumped back into the mash tun and mixed in thoroughly. This should bring the mash temperature to 60 to 65 °C. The mash is stirred until it has fully liquefied.

After that, the mash is rested for 15 minutes, followed by drawing off the wort, called *warmer Satz*, through the false bottom. Two thirds of it are added to the kettle, while one third is kept in the *Grand*. The wort in the kettle is slowly brought to a boil. Any foam or coagulating proteins on the top of wort are continuously skimmed off. The boiling wort is again added to the main mash and thoroughly mixed through. The resulting mash temperature should again be at around 65 °C. Then the thick portion of the mash is pumped into the kettle and boiled for 1 to 2 hours. Boiling is considered finished when no more new foam appears on top of the thick mash. The boiling mash is then mixed back into the main mash which should increase the mash temperature to 70 °C.

The wort kept in the *Grand* is then added to the kettle and the hops are added. The mash is then lautered and the clear wort from lautering is also added to the kettle which is brought to a boil.

According to Cassian, the advantage of this method is a more full-bodied beer that keeps better. He considered it to be obsolete and unusable at a large scale, as keeping large amounts of cool or just warm wort as required by the method could easily cause the formation of unwanted lactic acid.

In the Augsburg method, the mash is sparged after the first wort has run off. The second runnings are not combined with the first runnings though, but are rather turned into a light beer called *Hansl*.

(Source: [28, pp. 259–263])

4.4 Brewing Method in Bamberg

4.4.1 According to Johann Albert Joseph Seifert (1818)

Johann Seifert's work about brewing in Bamberg was published in 1818 and discusses all the peculiarities of the local breweries of the city compared to brewers in surrounding cities and the rest of Bamberg.

Seifert's description starts out with the right ratio of malt to water. 140 Pfund of barley malt and 5 5/8 Eimer of water are needed to brew 4 1/2 Eimer of "good beer", and an additional 3 3/8 Eimer of water to brew 2 1/4 Eimer of *Nachbier* from a second mash, which he calls *Hainslein* or *Koffent* [10, p. 17].

In terms of water quality, Seifert ranks the types of water by their source. He considers rain water to be of the best quality, but concedes that it is hard to acquire and that water cisterns to store rain water are uncommon in Germany. River water is the next-best water source in terms of quality. The worst according to Seifert is well water, as it needs to be boiled beforehand to be suitable for brewing. While he attributes the flavour differences between breweries to the water, he also describes how some breweries in Bamberg treat the water before brewing: by letting it sit in open vessels in the open air so that the sun can shine on it. This apparently helps gasses to come out of suspension, but is also a laborious tasks hence why many brewers shy away from it [10, pp. 15–17].

Mashing starts with doughing in the malt by only using a relatively small amount of water to wet the malt. The mash tun is prepared in a particular way: to add water, it is equipped with a *Pfaff* for underletting. It needs to be fit exactly with the false bottom which is removable and secured so that it doesn't come loose during mashing. In the dead space between mash tun bottom and false bottom, called *Sumpf* (lit. *swamp*), straw is added, presumably to help with filtering. On top of the false bottom, chaff is spread out. The malt is added to the mash tun, in a heap on the opposite side of the *Pfaff*.

When the mash tun is prepared, the malt is in the tun and the workers are ready, boiling and cold water, in a ratio of 1:2, is added via the *Pfaff* just to completely fill the dead space, plus a "hand high" of water over the level of the false bottom. Two workers then start mixing the crushed malt with the water using special mixing forks, until all the malt is wetted. This is hard work and might take a while. Each of them starts mixing at one side of the heap, going towards the middle until the forks meet there, and then go back again. When this is done, an indentation is formed in the middle of the mash, more hot and cold water is added by a third person in the same ratio as before, "as much as is necessary". It should still result in a fairly stiff mash. When the right amount of water is added and mixed in (Seifert doesn't give any particular amounts), the mash is covered and left to rest for 15 minutes.

Then, mashing commences: both boiling and cold water is added in a ratio of 2:1 through the *Pfaff* to lift the thick mash from the bottom. The amount of water added should be half of the total amount of water used for brewing this beer. During the underletting, two workers will try to prevent the water from breaking through from underneath. Only when this can't be prevented anymore, they start mashing and mixing the water with the mash. This first mash takes 15 minutes. After this first mashing, the mash is left to rest for an hour, then the tap is opened and the wort is recirculated until it is clear, then slowly run off onto the coolship.

This is followed by second mashing: the remaining water is added through the *Pfaff*, this time in a ratio of 3 parts hot water to 1 part of cold water. During this, the workers will thoroughly mix the water into the mash for a total of 15 minutes. Then, the mash is left to rest again for 15 minutes, and the wort is again run off as before into the coolship. Before this transfer, the wort from the first mash is transferred into a separate vessel.

Optionally, some brewers follow up with a third mash, consisting of hot water only, in the same way as before, i.e. the water is mixed into the mash for 15 minutes and left to rest for an hour until it is drawn off. According to Seifert, some brewers also simply use cold water for the third mashing, a practice he does not condone.

The next step is then to boil the wort. Some brewers combine all three runnings into one and boil that, while others only combine the first two runnings for their regular-strength beer, and use the last runnings to brew a *Nachbier* called *Hainslein* [10, pp. 19–26].

The next step is to boil the wort. In Bamberg, a particular technique called *Hopfenrösten* (lit. *hop roasting*) was employed by some brewers. The leaf hops are taken and boiled in a pan with just a small amount of clear wort. This causes most of the volatile aroma compounds to evaporate. These roasted hops are then combined with the wort and boiled for longer. Unfortunately, Seifert is not particularly clear on the length of the hop roasting or the total time of wort boiling. Seifert himself has criticised the technique, saying it evaporates the hop compounds that add aroma and flavour, leaving behind just pure bitterness, but that some Bamberg brewers have stuck to this technique.

For every Eimer of lager beer, 1 Pfund of hops was used. For other beers that were matured only for short periods of time, the amount of hops was lowered to 1/4 Pfund of hops, or in case high-quality hops were available, 1/2 Pfund. At the time, many Bamberg brewers still preferred using Bohemian hops. Seifert insists that local Franconian hops were equally suitable for brewing good beer, also insinuating without going into any specifics that some of the Bohemian hops imported into Bavaria may be forged, which he claims to have witnessed as a high school student in Chomutov/Komotau, near the border between Bohemia and Bavaria.

The boiled wort is then cooled, initially in several small flat vessels, until these are eventually combined in one large coolship. Seifert warns that the cooling process should be sufficiently quick, otherwise the wort may start fermenting spontaneously. He does not mention a particular maximum period, as this is something that needs to be guided by practical experience. When the wort is sufficiently cooled, it is then transferred to fermenting vessels. The wort shall be crystal clear at this point, which shall be achieved through proper care and good filtering through straw when running off the wort, but also through frequent recirculation beforehand. The wort shall also be sweet, to indicate proper conversion. Sweet wort will ensure that the resulting beer will be good, according to Seifert.

In the fermentation vessels, the yeast is added. It is only added when the wort is fully cooled down. Seifert recommends using thermometers, in particular ones of the Réaumur or Fahrenheit scale. The proper temperature for adding yeast according to him 10 to 20 Réaumur (12.5-25°C), and for *Nachbier* 15 to 20 Réaumur (18.75-25°C). The particular yeast used in Bamberg is bottom-fermenting. It is propagated by harvesting the bottom yeast from the bottom of the fermentation vessels.

For long-term keeping, the bottom sediment on lagering casks is also harvested and stored in sealable containers, or by drying the bottom yeast on straw wreaths. Seifert also describes another method: after the last brew of the season, yeast is harvested and put into a cloth which is then tied together and put in a vessel with cold ash. After a day or a bit longer, the ash will have drawn out much of the humidity from the yeast in the cloth. This yeast can then be slowly dried at a very moderate heat near an oven, and then kept in a bag. To use the yeast, it could simply be rehydrated. In yet another method, Seifert explains that the yeast sediment from lagering casks can be harvested and washed, then covered with oil and protected from air by tightly covering it with an ox bladder. Yeast kept that way can be stored at low temperatures for many months.

Historic lagering casks at the Franconian Brewery Museum in Bamberg

Seifert also mentions that brewers in Bamberg sometimes use top-cropped yeast. This practice is only used sparingly, for example for the first brew of the season, and if available, bottom yeast from other brewers is used preferably. Typically, this would have been from countryside brewers, as they started their brewing season earlier than the city brewers. They then supplied the city brewers with sufficient bottom-fermenting yeast. In Seifert's description of top-cropped yeast, it is not clear whether this was true top-fermenting yeast, or only top-cropped from a true bottom-fermenting yeast.

(Source: [10, pp. 26–44])

4.4.2 According to Johann Philipp Christian Muntz (1836)

Brewing starts by crushing the malt that was moistened a day before crushing. It is then brought to the mash tun. The brewing water in the kettle is brought to a boil, then cooled down slightly by adding cold water to stop the boil, and then added to the mash tun through the *Pfaff* so that the malt is lifted by the water through the false bottom. When most of the water has been transferred, the malt is mashed through for a bit more than 15 minutes. Then any remaining water in the kettle is removed, the wort is drawn off from the mash, put in the kettle, and boiled for 30 minutes. After this, the wort is added back to the mash via the *Pfaff*. The malt is lifted that way, but does not get mashed through.

More water is added to the kettle, brought to a boil, and added to the mash, again through the *Pfaff*, to add as much water as is necessary for one batch of beer. The mash is properly mixed through for 30 minutes, then the wort is drawn off. The kettle gets cleaned, and hops are then added to the kettle and boiled with just enough water or wort so that it's fully immersed. The hops are constantly stirred and boil for 30 to 45 minutes. Then the remaining wort is added and boiled. Some brewers boil for 90 minutes, others for 120 to 150 minutes. Every brewer seems to have their own method in this regard, but all beers turn out to be good. After the boil, the wort is cooled on coolships and then transferred to fermenters, where yeast is added.

In Bamberg, both bottom and top fermentation are in use. *Märzenbiere* are all fermented with bottom-fermenting yeast which usually takes about 13 to 14 days. Any beers that shall be served within 3, 4 or 6 weeks are fermented with top-cropped yeast and are finished fermenting after 7 days.

One particular method is also common in Bamberg: when the yeast has fully formed on top of the fermenting beer, malt flour is sprinkled on top of the yeast, and a birch broom is used to mix it all into the beer. This is supposed to produce more yeast. When fermentation is finished, any remaining yeast on top is removed, and the beer is filled into casks in the cellar. Unlike in other parts of Bavaria, the casks in Bamberg are not pitched with resin, but only burned out with sulphur. *Lagerbiere* also do not get bunged up, but the bunghole is only covered with a piece of slate. This method can only be used with bottom-fermented beers, as top-fermented ones would quickly go sour.

The remaining mash in the mash tun is again mashed with some of the remaining water, the wort drawn off, boiled with the spent hops from the first beer, cooled on the coolship, and then moved to a fermenter where yeast is added. The result is a light, clear drink that will last at least 6 weeks. Bambergers call this beer *Heinzele*. Some brewers sell it separately, while others blend it with beer.

(Source: [29, pp. 118–121])

4.4.3 According to Johann Adam Messerschmitt (1836)

Messerschmitt starts by boiling water from the well for up to 3 hours. The reason is to precipitate any matter that is dissolved in it. The boiling water is then diluted using cold water to a temperature of 64°R (80°C). This process is called *Abschrecken*. The malt is then added to the mash tun, so that it is heaped up more towards the sides of the mash tun and thinner in the middle. The mash tun has a *Pfaff* for underletting water. The hot water is poured through the *Pfaff* so that it lifts the malt, which then needs to swim on top of the water "like a cake".

Then the *Aufmaischen* begins: four people use special mash paddles to lift and sieve the mash so the malt is properly mixed with the water. This is done for 15 to 20 minutes, sometimes up to 30 minutes, depending on the brewmaster's opinion. After this first mash, the tap is opened to slowly draw off a thin mash, typically through a false bottom. The thin mash should be free from particles and look like buttermilk, and is scooped into the kettle. This is called the *Läuterungsmaisch*, which Messerschmitt attributes with making the Bamberg beer unique. When the kettle is filled by two thirds with mash, it is heated to bring it to a boil of 60 to 75 minutes.

After the boil time, some of the boiled thin mash is poured back through the *Pfaff*, while the rest is simply poured on top of the mash. The mash gets mixed through, while at the same time, the kettle gets cleaned. When the mashing is done, it is left to rest. A bit of clear thin mash has been reserved earlier which is again put in the kettle, and the weighed hops are added and boiled. For every 6 Scheffel of malt, 20 to 25 Pfund of hops are used for Winterbier, or 30 to 40 Pfund for Sommerbier.

During the hop boil, the wort is drawn off from the mash tun so that it is clear, and then scooped into the kettle. When the kettle is two thirds full, the fire is increased to bring the complete wort to a boil. The complete wort is then boiled for 2 hours if it is Winterbier, or up to 3 hours if it is Sommerbier.

When the boil is finished, the beer is then scooped into a coolship. Some brewers apparently also let the wort cool in the kettle, but this can make it *kesselroth* (lit. *kettle red*). Messerschmitt recommends not to let the wort cool for too long, as the precipitated matter can go back into solution and make the wort murky. It is better to move wort at 10°R (12.5°C) after 10 hours into the fermentation cellar than at 8°R (10°C) after 20 hours. The ideal temperature for adding yeast to the wort should be 8 to 10 °R.

In the fermentation cellar, the beer yeast, called *Grund* or *Gährstoff*, is added. For 30 Eimer of beer, 18 Maß of quality *Grund* are added.

Unfortunately, Messerschmitt is very vague on the amounts of water used when brewing, as well as the volume of the *Läuterungsmaisch* that is drawn off. We also don't learn about the mash temperature after the thin mash is mixed back.

(Source: [12, pp. 6–17])

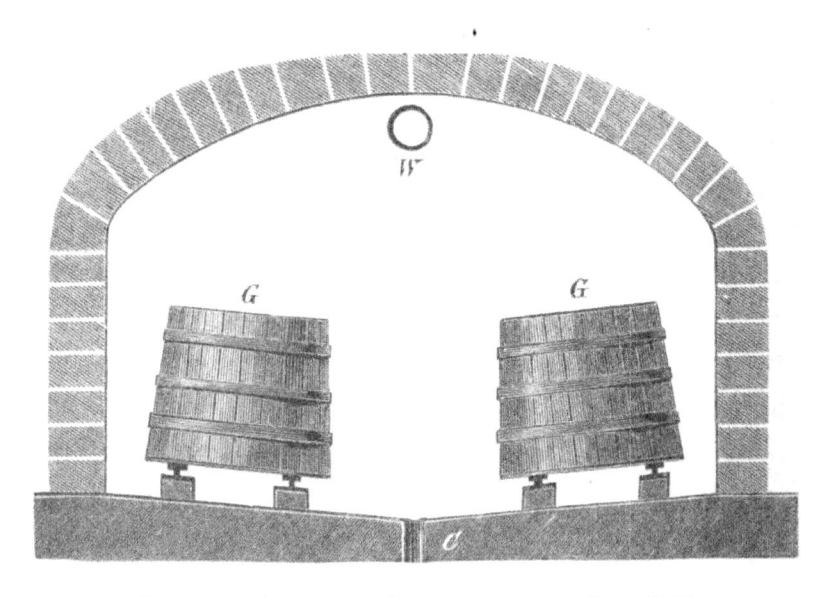

How to place open fermenters in cellars [28]

4.4.4 Nachbier According to Johann Adam Messerschmitt (1836)

Nachbier production begins when all the wort has been drawn off the mash, as described in the previous section. The top layer of the mash is then removed, the mash is hacked up using a shovel, and water is added. Messerschmitt preferred to use cold well water to extract the remaining sugar, but mentioned that other breweries were also using hot water.

When the boiled first wort has been removed from the kettle, the second runnings are being lautered off and scooped into the kettle. It should run off clear and pale. If the liquid remains in contact with the mash for too long, it can turn sour and is not usable for further brewing.

When these second runnings get boiled, 2 to 8 Pfund of hops are added to the wort. The boil itself needs to be timed so that the coolship has been emptied from the first brew before the *Nachbier* wort can be added to it.

When the wort has been cooled to 17°C, yeast was added at a rate of 3 to 8 Maß. Fermentation should be finished within 2 days. The beer is then put into casks where it undergoes a secondary fermentation.

(Source: [12, pp. 31–34])

4.4.5 According to A. Herrmann (1839)

In Bamberg, *Märzenbier* was always brewed in a bottom-fermented fashion which usually took 12 to 14 days, while beers that needed to be served quickly were brewed top-fermented which took 7 to 8 days and produced a very clear beer. Some brewers believed that they could produce more harvestable yeast by mixing malt flour into the fermenting beer.

The Bamberg breweries are described as generally having good rock cellars that are as deep as 100 Schuh (29.2 meters) below surface and large enough to fit in casks with volumes between 20 to 30 Eimer (13.7 to 20.5 hl).

The brewing method itself is described as follows:

Water in the kettle is brought to a boil. Cold water is then added to cool it down, after which it is scooped into the mash tun via a *Pfaff*. The mash tun is already filled with crushed malt, so the water gets in contact with the malt through the false bottom. Water is added until the malt is slightly covered with water. The brewers then start with the mashing which takes about 30 minutes. After that, all the wort is drawn off from the mash, scooped into the kettle, brought to a boil, and added back to the mash through the *Pfaff*. The mash is not mixed through at this point and left to rest.

Then more water is added to the kettle and brought to a boil, just enough that is necessary to add to the mash. When the water boils, it is again added to the mash via the *Pfaff*, and the

Various methods of placing casks in rock cellars [20]

mash is thoroughly mixed through for 30 minutes. Immediately afterwards, lautering begins and the collected wort is scooped into the kettle. Hops are added and the wort is brought to a boil over the course of about 45 minutes, while more wort is still added to the kettle. Then the whole wort is boiled for 90 minutes to 2 hours, depending on the brewer's opinion, and then cooled in a coolship.

During autumn and spring, it is often difficult to cool the wort further down than 12.5°C, while during the winter, it is easier to bring it down to 7.5°C.

In this approach, a considerable amount of sugar is left behind in the mash, so a *Nachbier* is produced. The top layer of the mash is taken off and used in distilling. Then the mash is hacked up and water is added, depending on how much *Nachbier* shall be brewed, but typically 30 to 40 Maß of water per Schäffel of malt. It is then left to rest for 45 minutes until wort is drawn off, scooped into the kettle, brought to a boil and boiled with the spent hops from the previous batch. It is then cooled in a coolship and fermented like regular beer.

Optionally, a third mash can be done, to get *Glattwasser* which is used for distilling. The spent grains are often sold as animal feed.

(Source: [13, pp. 54–59])

4.4.6 Franconian or Bamberg Method According to Friedrich Meyer (1847)

What makes this brewing method unique compared to other Bavarian brewing methods is that the malt itself is never boiled. Within Bavaria, it is only applied by Franconian breweries, mainly in Bamberg.

The crushed malt is added to the empty mash tun and spread out in such a way that more of it is kept towards the mash tun walls. In the meanwhile, water is brought to a boil in the kettle and is then cooled down by adding more cold water so that it reaches a temperature of 80°C. This water is then scooped into a *Pfaff* to underlet the malt which gets lifted up. The mash is then thoroughly mixed through for at least 20 minutes. The sticks used for mixing have a sieve or grid at the end to help with mixing. After mashing is complete, the mash tun tap is opened and liquid is drawn off, first at a slow rate, later faster. The liquid is hazy and is called the *Lautermeisch*. This is done until the kettle is about two-thirds full. The end of the runnings, which should be clear by then, are kept in the *Grand* which should be one-third to half full. It will later be used to add to the kettle as wort. The liquid in the kettle is brought to a boil and boiled for about 15 minutes.

This boiled liquid is then added back to the mash, initially through the *Pfaff*, later just directly onto the mash, which is mixed through thoroughly. After the kettle has been emptied and cleaned, the liquid kept back in the *Grand* is added to the kettle.

The process of drawing off *Lautermeisch*, boiling it and mixing it back may be done a second time to correct a perceived mashing error, in particular insufficient extraction of sugar during the first mash. This should happen very rarely.

The mash is left to rest only until it has settled down. The tap is then slowly opened to draw off clear wort.

While the mash is still resting, the required amount of hops are added to the kettle where it is mixed through and boiled for a brief period. The clear wort drawn off from the mash is then added to the boiling wort and hops in the kettle. While this happens, adding wort should happen at such a pace that the boil itself is not interrupted. In total, the wort is boiled for 1 to 2 hours. Schenkbier is boiled shorter, while Sommerbier is boiled for longer. When the boil is finished, the hot wort is immediately moved to the coolship. For 6 Schäffel of malt, 20 to 25 Pfund of hops are used in Winterbier or Schenkbier, while for Sommerbier, 30 to 40 Pfund of hops are used.

(Source: [11, pp. 195–199])

4.4.7 According to Philipp Heiß (1860)

The malt is spread out in the mash tun so that it is deeper in the middle and piled higher on the sides of the mash tun. The mash tun is constructed with a false bottom and a *Pfaffe*, a pipe to allow underletting through the false bottom. Within the *Pfaffe* is a long stick to open and close a small hole that is used for drawing off wort from the mash tun.

Water is brought to a boil in the kettle and then cooled down with cold water to a temperature of 80°C. It is then scooped into the *Pfaffe* so that it lifts the malt from underneath. The malt should swim on top of the water like a cake. When all the water is added, then it is mashed for 30 minutes using special mash paddles that help lift and "sieve" the malt.

After this mash step has been finished, the tap is slowly opened and wort drawn off into the *Grand* which is then moved to the kettle. When all the wort has been drawn off, about half of the Grand shall remain filled. The wort collected in the kettle is called *Lautermaisch*. It is brought to a boil and boiled for 75 minutes. 20 to 24 buckets of freshly boiled wort are poured through the *Pfaffe* to help dissolve some of the particles underneath the false bottom, then the remaining boiled wort is scooped on top of the mash. Then the mash is thoroughly mixed through for about 30 minutes and eventually left to rest. As soon as the kettle has been emptied and cleaned, the wort kept in the *Grand* is added to it in order to prevent the kettle from getting heat-damaged.

Then, hops are added to the kettle and a small fire is started underneath to start the hop boil. The hops are mixed with the wort during the boil. In terms of quantity, 20 to 25 Pfund of hops are used for Winterbier when it is brewed from 6 Schäffel of malt, while 30 to 40 Pfund are used when Sommerbier is brewed from the same amount of malt.

When the mash has settled sufficiently, wort is drawn off and added to the kettle until it is two-thirds full. The fire underneath is then increased to bring the wort to a boil, which is then boiled until hot break forms. It is then moved to coolships.

(Source: [22, pp. 146–148])

Historic open fermenters at the Franconian Brewery Museum in Bamberg

4.4.8 Hansle, According to Philipp Heiß (1860)

Nachbier or *Hansle* was a necessary product in Bamberg during the 19th century, not only as an inexpensive drink for poor people, but also as a mixer of sorts. Some people liked to mix their Lagerbier with Hansle (often two parts Lagerbier to one part Hansle) to lower the strength.

As described in the previous section, no second mash is done to collect second runnings. This is done deliberately to be able to brew more Nachbier. To do so, fresh well water is added to the mash until the boiled wort of the previous brew has been transferred to the coolship. When the Hansle wort is boiled, the hops from the previous brew are either reused for it, or only a small amount of 6 to 8 Pfund of fresh hops per 6 Schäffel of malt are added. From that amount of malt, at least 10 to 12 Eimer can be produced. The wort itself is only briefly boiled, and then fermented and lagered separately.

(Source: [22, p. 148])

4.4.9 Franconian Method According to Franz Cassian (1887)

The Franconian method as described by Franz Cassian uses 700 litres of water per 100 kg of malt. The crushed malt is added dry to the mash tun and then hot water at about 80 to 85 °C is added and thoroughly mixed with the malt until the mash has reached a temperature of about 62 to 63 °C. The mash is then left to rest. The entire wort is then lautered and added to the kettle where it is quickly brought to a boil. Any foam on top of the wort is skimmed off. After boiling the wort for 45 minutes, it is mixed back into the main mash which should result in a mash temperature of 75 °C. After this, the mash is left to rest for an hour.

Then a small amount of wort, about 1/10 of the total amount, is drawn off, added to the kettle together with the hops and boiled for about 30 minutes. During that time, the remaining wort is drawn off. After the 30 minute boil, the rest of the wort is added to the kettle and boiled for an unspecified amount of time.

The mash is sparged, but the resulting wort is not combined with the first runnings, but rather used to brew a light beer called *Hansl*.

(Source: [28, pp. 261–263])

4.5 Kulmbacher Brewing Method, According to Philipp Heiß (1860)

The malt is conditioned with 12 to 15 Maß of water per Schäffel of malt prior to crushing. The malt is only coarsely crushed and added dry into a simple mash tun consisting of a wooden false bottom and a *Pfaffen*. In the kettle, a certain amount of water is heated up to 50°C and then added through the *Pfaffen*, but only just enough to wet all the malt. In the kettle, there must be enough water left for the next mashing.

This water is then brought to a boil while the malt is being stirred using stirring rakes to thoroughly mix it with the water. When the water is fully boiling, it is also added through the *Pfaffen* and thoroughly mixed in for another 30 minutes. The final mash temperature should be at 52 to 56°C.

When the liquid slightly separates from the malt, it is drawn off completely, scooped or pumped over into the kettle, brought to a boil, and then thoroughly mixed back into the main mash for at least 45 minutes. This should increase the temperature of the mash to 62 to 67°C. A bit of wort shall remain in the kettle to which the hops as well as a few Eimer of cold water are added. The hops are then mixed into the wort in the kettle.

Towards the end of this rest, the liquid in the kettle is brought to a boil and boiled for about 8 to 12 minutes. This is called *Hopfenrösten* (hop roasting).

Then the mash tun valves are opened and lautering begins. Collected wort is scooped over into the kettle to stop the hop roasting. When all wort has been collected, cold water is poured over the mash to collect second runnings which are also added to the kettle. This can be repeated once more to collect *Glattwasser* which is not added to the kettle.

The wort in the kettle is then boiled until about 20% of it is evaporated. This could take up to 4 to 5 hours depending on the fire and the fuel. It is then left to stand for another 15 to 30 minutes in the kettle. The wort is then poured through a hop strainer onto the coolship.

As this type of beer is often brewed for export, 5 Eimer of both Sommer- and Winterbier are brewed from 1 Schäffel of malt. For Winterbier, 2.5 Pfund of hops are added per Schäffel of malt, or 0.5 Pfund per Eimer of beer, while for Sommerbier, up to 7 Pfund of hops or 1.5 Pfund per Eimer of beer can be added, depending on when it is brewed and how long it needs to keep through the summer. For especially long lagering or exports that are going very far, even more hops can be added to further fortify the beer.

In terms of hops, Sommerbier was exclusively brewed with hops of the highest quality, but even for Winterbier, only hops from the latest harvest were used.

(Source: [22, pp. 149–152])

4.6 White Beer

4.6.1 White Beer Brewing Method According to Friedrich Meyer (1847)

White beer is brewed from pale barley malt with a small amount of pale wheat malt, usually in a ratio of 1 Metze of wheat malt per

Schäffel of barley malt. The amount of a Schäffel of malt should produce 8 Eimer of white beer, and a total amount of 15 Eimer of water will be required to brew it.

Part of the water is filled into the kettle and brought to a boil, while the remaining water is put cold into the mash tun. The crushed malt is then added on top of the water in the mash tun and left to rest for 2 hours.

After these 2 hours, a quantity of "kalter Satz" is drawn off from the mash tun. Then hot water is scooped from the kettle into the mash tun and is thoroughly mixed together with the malt and the cold water until the mash has reached a temperature of 45 to 47.5°C. This is then left to rest for 10 minutes.

In the meantime, the "kalter Satz" drawn off earlier is transferred to the kettle to cool down the remaining hot water. After the 10 minute rest, wort is drawn off from the mash tun and added to the kettle to bring the level back to where it was when it was initially filled with water. At the same time, the content of the kettle is getting heated up, ideally so that it is close to boiling when the kettle is full.

Then the *warmer Satz* is drawn off from the mash, about 1.5 to 2 Eimer per Schäffel of malt, which is then transferred to the coolship. Then a bit more of wort is drawn off and kept in the *Grand* to later cool off the kettle.

The liquid in the kettle is then scooped on top of the mash and thoroughly mixed in until the mash has reached a temperature of 57.5 to 60°C. The liquid in the *Grand* is added to the kettle in the meantime to cool it off. Then the complete mash is scooped over into the kettle, brought to a boil and boiled for 30 to 45 minutes.

The boiled mash is then scooped back and thoroughly mixed through, after which it is left to rest for about 30 minutes, during which the kettle gets cleaned out and filled with the *warmer Satz* that was kept in the coolship.

Then lautering begins by drawing off wort from the mash tun and adding it to the kettle. The kettle is getting heated, ideally so that it starts boiling shortly after it has been completely filled. While the wort in the kettle is heating up, a thick layer of foam forms on top which needs to be skimmed off. When the wort has started boiling and the foam on top has been taken off, hops are added, usually 1 Pfund of hops per 8 or 9 Eimer of beer or per Schäffel of malt used in brewing. In total, the wort is boiled for 45 minutes.

The wort is then cooled off down to a temperature 22.5°C which is when the top-fermenting white beer yeast is added.

(Source: [11, pp. 203–208])

4.6.2 White Wheat Beer Brewing Method According to Friedrich Meyer (1847)

Similar to the white barley beer in the previous section, white beer can also be brewed from wheat. This beer is typically served fresh, but keeps well for weeks or even months. It was considered to be better when refermented in sealed jugs.

This beer was brewed using a triple decoction mash with two thick mashes and one thin mash, similar to the Old Bavarian brewing method. The water quantity to use depended on the strength of the beer to brew. As an example, this description says that if you wanted to brew 8 Eimer of wheat beer from one Schäffel of wheat malt, you needed 15 Eimer of water. This amount of water is divided into a larger and a smaller portion. The larger part is brought to a boil in the kettle, while the smaller part is added to the mash tun at "normal" temperature (no specific temperature is provided). The crushed malt is then added to the mash tun, stirred in so that all clumps have broken up and then left to rest for 1 to 2 hours, while the water in the kettle starts to boil.

When the water boils, the first mash is started by stirring the mash while the hot water is added to it. This continues until the mash has reached a temperature of 42 to 45°C. Immediately, the mash is scooped into the kettle, initially enough thin mash to substantially cool down the remaining hot water in the kettle, only later more thick parts of the mash until it is about one half full. The mash in the kettle is then brought to a boil and boiled for 30 minutes.

Then the second mash begins: the mash from the kettle is scooped back into the mash tun under constant stirring until the main mash has reached a temperature of 55 to 57°C. When this is done, mash is scooped from the mash tun back into the kettle in the same way as before, first thin mash to cool the remaining mash in the kettle, then thick mash until it is about two thirds full. This mash is again brought to a boil and boiled for 45 minutes.

Then the third mash begins: again, the mash from the kettle is scooped back into the mash tun under constant stirring until the main mash has reached a temperature of 62 to 65°C. When this is done, thin mash is scooped from the main mash back into the kettle until the kettle is half full. Then the mash is rested for 10 minutes. After this brief rest, thin mash is drawn off and added to the kettle until the mash volume in the kettle has reached about the same volume as the amount of water in it before the first mash. Then the mash in the kettle is brought to a boil. During this, the *Biergrand* underneath the mash tun is cleaned and wort is drawn off which will later be used to add to the kettle to protect it against the heat.

As soon as the mash in the kettle has started boiling, the fourth and final mash begins: all the mash is scooped back into the mash tun under constant stirring. When all the mash has been moved, stirring continues for a little longer, then the mash is left to rest for 30 minutes.

The kettle is then cleaned and the wort kept in the *Biergrand* is added to it. Then wort is drawn off from the mash tun and added to the kettle where it is brought to a boil. Any foam that forms on top gets skimmed off. When the foam has been removed, fresh hops, at a rate of about one Pfund per Schäffel of malt, are added to the wort which is then boiled for 45 minutes.

Then the wort is transferred to the coolship and carefully cooled down to 22.5°C. Some of the wort in the coolship is used to stir into the top-fermenting yeast which then has some time to get active and is later added to the wort. The yeast is then added to the wort in a separate tun and thoroughly mixed through at a rate of about 4 to 6 Maß per Schäffel of malt.

The freshly inoculated wort is then filled into cleaned casks. The casks are positioned in such a way that the bunghole are slightly sideways so that any yeast that gets later ejected during fermentation can run off into a separate vessel. If multiple casks are used for fermentation, they should be set up in pairs so that two casks can eject their yeast into the same vessel underneath. From these vessels, the yeast is skimmed off and cleaned, while the liquid is used to top up the casks.

Yeast getting ejected from a fermentation cask with a bunghole and getting caught in a separate vessel [30]

When the fermentation has finished, the casks are bunged up and sent out. The beer should be ready for consumption within 8 days.

(Source: [11, pp. 212–220])

4.6.3 White Beer According to Philipp Heiß (1860)

Bavarian White Beers were top-fermented beers that were either brewed from pale barley malt, wheat malt, or a combination thereof. Due to its top-fermented nature, it was a beer type that could be brewed during the whole year.

Unlike brown beer, white beers were not regulated in terms of their strength. This led to brewers in the country side brewing relatively weak beer that was sold for a cheap price (2 Kreuzer per Maß) and thus was popular amongst workers. Brewers also earned additional money with the sale of yeast. In some cases, just selling the yeast covered all the brewing costs, leaving the brewer with more profit.

Philipp Heiß describes a *better* type of white beer, where 8 Eimer of beer were brewed from one Schäffel of barley malt. Quite often, an additional 1 Metze of wheat malt was added. The overall amount of water required was 14 Eimer. The process described here is essentially a form of *Satzbrauen*.

Initially, the water is divided between mash tun and kettle. The crushed malt is then doughed in with the cold water and left to rest for about 2 hours. When this time is nearly over, 4 to 5 Eimer of wort are drawn off and put aside. This is the *kalter Satz*. The water in the kettle is brought to a boil and mixed into the mash under constant stirring until the mash has reached a temperature of about 45 to 47°C.

The kalter Satz is then added to the kettle and mixed with the remaining hot water, and the mash is rested for 15 minutes. Then the mash tun valves are opened and *Lautermaisch* (thin mash) is drawn off as quickly as possible into the *Grand* underneath, from where it is scooped into the kettle. There it is being brought to a boil while the kettle is still getting filled. When enough *Lautermaisch* has been collected, the valves are closed, the *Grand* is emptied and the valves are reopened to collect the *warmer Satz*, typically 2 Eimer of *warmer Satz* per Schäffel of malt. It is then moved to the coolship. Then more liquid is drawn off that is later used to cool down the kettle.

When the thin mash has been brought to a boil, it immediately gets scooped back under constant stirring until the main mash has reached a temperature of 57 to 60°C. The thin mash in the *Grand* as well as the main mash are then completely moved to the kettle, brought to a boil and boiled for 30 to 45 minutes. It is then moved back into the mash tun and thoroughly mixed through. At the end of mashing, it shall be at a temperature of 81 to 88°C. It is then left to rest for 30 minutes.

In the meanwhile, the kettle gets cleaned and the *warmer Satz* that was kept on the coolship is added to it. Then lautering begins, and wort is drawn off from the mash and added to the kettle. When the kettle is half full, it is slowly brought to a boil while the remaining wort is moved to the kettle. Any foam to forms on the top gets skimmed off. When the wort boils, hops are added at a rate of about 1 Pfund per Schäffel of malt, and boiled for 60 minutes.

When the boil is finished, the wort is moved to the coolship where it is cooled down to 17 to 19°C. From the coolship, the wort is moved to a separate tun where the yeast is added and thoroughly mixed into the wort.

(Source: [22, pp. 152–154])

4.6.4 Kelheim White Beer According to Philipp Heiß (1860)

According to Philipp Heiß, most white beer in Bavaria at the time was brewed from two thirds barley malt and one third wheat malt. An exception to that was the white beer brewed in Kelheim that was brewed from 100% finely ground wheat malt.

The complete amount of water is divided up between mash tun and kettle so that the mash tun contains slightly more water than the kettle. For example, 6 Schäffel of dry wheat malt are ground and then mashed in with 48 Eimer of fresh water in mash tun. This mash is then left to rest for 2 hours. After that, the boiling water from the kettle, 38 Eimer in total, is added to the mash while constantly stirring so that the mash reaches a temperature of 44°C.

Then, 36 Eimer of thick mash are scooped from the mash tun to the kettle and brought to a boil. As soon as the boil starts, it is scooped back into the mash tun and thoroughly mashed through for 30 minutes. The resulting mash temperature should be 60°C.

Again, 36 Eimer of thick mash are scooped from the mash tun to the kettle and brought to a boil, where it is then boiled for 30 minutes. After this, it is mixed back into the main mash under constant stirring. When the kettle has been emptied, 12 Eimer of thin mash are drawn off and added to the kettle to protect it from the fire damage. The main mash meanwhile gets mashed through for another 30 minutes and should reach about 68°C.

While mashing is ongoing, the *Biergrand* gets cleaned and filled with wort that is drawn off from the mash tun until it runs clear. Any wort that is not clear is scooped back into the mash tun. As soon as the wort runs clear, the thin mash in the kettle is brought to a boil and as soon as it boils, is scooped back into the mash tun where mashing commences for another 30 minutes. The mashing was done with such a force so that the mash temperature drops to about 64°C, below the temperature after the second mash.

As soon as the kettle has been emptied, the wort collected in the *Grand* is added to it along with 8 Pfund of ordinary country-side hops. Another *Grand* full of clear wort is drawn off which is added to the kettle, then the mash tun valves are closed and the mash is left to rest for 30 minutes.

Since drawing off wort from a 100% wheat malt mash is difficult, the mash tuns didn't just have a tap at the bottom, but had holes on the side of the mash tun at all levels that were usually bunged up but could be opened to draw off wort from the top of the mash using a linen hosepipe. When all the wort was collected, the top layer of the mash was removed and hot water was scooped on top of it which again was run off and added to the kettle.

(Source: [22, pp. 155–157])

Appendix A

Historic Bavarian Units

In this book, historic units of measurements are used. In order to allow a meaningful interpretation, this section lists all conversions of historic units to modern units as well as their relationship to each other.

1 Maß = 1.069 l

1 Eimer (Biereimer) = 64 Maß = 68.416 l

1 Metze = 34 2/3 Maß = 37.05960 l

1 Scheffel (Schäffel) = 6 Metzen = 208 Maß = 222.35762 l

1 Brauhausschäffel = 12 Maß = 12.828 l

1 Pfund = 561.288 g (before 1811)

1 Pfund = 560 g (from 1811 onward)

1 Zentner (Centner) = 100 Pfund

1 Zollpfund = 500 g (since 1854)

1 Schuh (Fuß) = 292 mm

A measuring cylinder from 1809, containing exactly 1 Bavarian Maß

Appendix B

Beer Analyses

B.1 Analyses of Munich Beers, 1866

Brewery	Beer Type	SG	ABW %	Extract %
Hofbräuhaus	Bockbier	1.02467	5.08	7.83
– " –	Sommerbier	1.0141	3.88	4.93
– " –	Weißbier	1.01288	3.51	4.37
– " –	Weißes Bockbier	1.02000	4.41	4.55
Spatenbräu	Bockbier	1.02678	5.23	8.50
Zacherl	Salvatorbier	1.03327	4.49	9.63
Löwenbräu	Winterbier	1.0170	3.00	5.92

(Source: [31])

B.2 Analyses of Munich Summer Beers of 1867

Brewery	Date	SG	ABW %	Extract %	OG
Hofbräuhaus	June 13	1.0170	3.61	5.87	12.61
– " –	June 14	1.0172	3.56	5.90	12.69
Spatenbräu	June 27	1.0207	3.21	6.61	12.66
– " –	July 4	1.0178	3.45	6.01	12.49
Löwenbräu	July 1	1.0181	3.72	6.20	13.14
– " –	July 2	1.0189	3.61	6.35	13.22
Singlspieler	July 3	1.0185	3.56	6.22	12.84
– " –	July 9	1.0191	3.63	6.40	13.17
Augustiner	July 4	1.0198	3.46	6.50	13.10
– " –	July 10	1.0202	3.32	6.54	12.75
G. Pschorr	July 12	1.0160	3.61	5.62	12.44
– " –	July 16	1.0153	3.60	5.42	12.25
Schleibinger	July 17	1.0180	3.99	6.26	13.69
– " –	July 24	1.0192	3.84	6.32	13.73
Hacker	July 29	1.0177	3.73	6.12	13.20
– " –	July 30	1.0178	3.74	6.13	13.18
Zacherl	August 1	1.0190	3.73	6.49	13.75
– " –	August 5	1.0177	3.98	6.22	13.74
Leist	August 2	1.0181	3.39	6.05	12.41
– " –	August 5	1.0183	3.39	6.11	12.51

The content of alcohol by weight (ABW) has been determined according to the Balling method. OG is in °Balling.

(Source: [32])

B.3 Analyses of Zacherl Beers, 1874-1876

Beer Type	SG	ABW %	Extract %	OG
Salvator 1874	1.0267	4.22	8.58	16.71
Salvator 1875	1.028	4.64	9.078	17.8
Salvator 1876	1.0343	4.19	10.43	18.46

Beer Type	SG	ABW %	Extract %	OG
Zacherl Schenkbier	1.0191	3.4	6.3	-

(Source: [33])

B.4 Beer Analyses, 1878

Beer/Brewery	SG	ABW %	Extract %	OG (°Balling)
Helles Culmbacher	1.0153	3.59	6.10	13.28
Dunkles Culmbacher	1.0182	3.62	7.53	14.77
Weihenstephaner	1.0147	4.06	5.49	13.61
Erlanger	1.0175	3.98	6.59	14.55
Niklas in Erlangen	1.0190	3.40	7.85	14.65
Nürnberger	1.0158	3.77	6.18	13.72

(Source: [34])

B.5 Beer Analyses of Salvatorbier, 1896

Brewery, Beer	SG	ABW %	Extract %	OG (°Balling)
Aktienbr. Nürnberg	1.0311	5.24	12.12	19.84
Lederer, Nürnberg	1.0326	4.19	10.32	18.20
Löwenbräu, Nürnberg	1.0316	4.20	9.71	17.60
Tucher Nürnberg	1.0241	4.81	8.16	17.22
Geismann, Fürth	1.0350	5.92	11.14	22.00
Knöllinger, Schwabach	1.0392	3.78	11.42	18.45
Spatenbräu, München	1.0340	5.00	10.72	20.00
Zacherlbräu, München	1.0345	4.39	10.57	18.77
Lederer, Nürnberg	1.0321	4.68	7.08	16.00

(Source: [35])

Appendix C

Production Statistics

C.1 Number of Bavarian Breweries and their Production, 1859-1871

Year	Breweries	Beer Production (Eimer)	Value (florin)
1859/1860	5,123	10,313,415	52,316,516
1860/1861	5,122	7,934,157	53,510,172
1861/1862	5,417	10,672,578	54,973,104
1862/1863	5,424	11,878,698	60,945,723
1863/1864	5,518	12,494,133	66,779,412
1864/1865	5,548	12,935,133	65,881,027
1865/1866	5,871	13,667,744	75,042,533
1866/1867	5,145	12,137,462	71,691,744
1867/1868	5,091	11,800,805	69,949,000
1868/1869	5,105	12,632,595	84,044,214
1869/1870	5,137	11,803,549	68,245,459
1871	5,177	13,457,326	–

(Source: [36, p. 43])

C.2 Beer Production in Eimer by Beer Type, 1859-1871

Year	Schankbier	Lagerbier	Luxury Beer	White Beer
1859/1860	4,467,269	5,053,913	81,444	440,789
1860/1861	3,194,556	4,184,599	76,679	478,323
1861/1862	4,963,519	5,143,948	82,788	482,323
1862/1863	5,455,097	5,827,449	108,952	487,200
1863/1864	5,619,932	6,143,325	271,498	459,378
1864/1865	5,789,768	6,337,395	272,960	535,107
1865/1866	6,024,806	7,152,233	100,622	390,083
1866/1867	5,460,559	6,185,191	125,470	366,242
1867/1868	5,277,374	5,985,036	120,052	418,343
1868/1869	5,696,285	6,447,860	136,418	352,032
1869/1870	5,398,450	5,966,380	114,493	324,226
1871	6,263,987	6,625,452	194,127	373,760

The amounts of malt used are in Schäffel.

(Source: [36, p. 44])

Acknowledgements and Dedications

To my wife Louise, who for the third time put up with me getting all worked up about yet another niche beer history topic.

To all the doctors and nurses at Charité Virchow hospital ward 43, without whom I most likely would not have been here anymore to write this book.

Many thanks go out to my good friend Ben Palmer, who thoroughly proof-read this book and gave me lots of valuable feedback, and for the many fun, entertaining and educational hours with and about beer and brewing.

Bibliography

1. Meyer, Friedrich. *Die bayerische Bierbrauerei oder die Brauerei der braunen Biere und des weißen Gerstenbieres, wie solche in den vorzüglichsten Brauereien in Bayern dermalen betrieben wird, dann die mit der Bierbrauerei verbundene Branntweinbrennerei, Fruchtessigsiederei und das einem Brauer Nöthige über den Hopfen und den Hopfenbau, ein Lehrbuch für jeden, der die Bierbrauerei erlernen, oder auch überhaupt sich von dem practischen Betriebe derselben selbst unterrichten will.* Ansbach, 1830. https://play.google.com/books/reader?id=1f9CAAAAcAAJ

2. Gattinger, K. *Bier und Landesherrschaft: das Weißbiermonopol der Wittelsbacher unter Maximilian I. von Bayern ; 1598 - 1651.* Lipp, 2007. ed. lipp. ISBN 9783874907576.

3. Müller, P. *Handbuch für Bierbrauer, eine wissenschaftlich-praktische Anleitung zum Bierbrauen im ganzen Umfange des Gewerbes : mit Rücksicht auf die neuesten Erfahrungen und Verbesserungen im Braufache, und unter Beifügung der verschiedenen Braumethoden in Baiern und anderen Ländern.* Braunschweig, 1854. https://play.google.com/books/reader?id=UTw7AAAAcAAJ

4. Prechtl, Johann Baptist. *Zur Geschichte des bayerischen Bieres.* 1879. https://opacplus.bsb-muenchen.de/title/BV020362403

5. Moshamm, Franz Xaver von. *Ueber das Bierbraurecht in Baiern*. 1791. https://www.digitale-sammlungen.de/de/view/bsb10376745

6. Struve, Emil. *Die Entwicklung des bayerischen Braugewerbes im neunzehnten Jahrhundert. Ein Beitrag zur deutschen Gewerbegeschichte der Neuzeit*. 1893. https://archive.org/details/dieentwicklungd00strugoog

7. Map of the Kingdom of Bavaria.. 1808. https://commons.wikimedia.org/wiki/File:Karte_Bayern_1808.jpg

8. Prior, Dr. Eugen. *Erlaubtes und Verbotenes im bayerichen Brauereiwesen*. Würzburg, 1885.

9. Scharl, Benno. *Beschreibung der Braunbier-Brauerey im Königreiche Baiern*. Munich, 1814. https://www.bavarikon.de/object/bav:BSB-MDZ-00000BSB10298820

10. Seifert, Johann Albert Joseph. *Das Bamberger Bier*. Bamberg, 1818. https://play.google.com/books/reader?id=nyFGz5LXDlwC

11. Meyer, Friedrich. *Die bayerische Bierbrauerei in allen ihren Theilen und wie solche in den vorzüglichsten Bierbrauerein im Königreiche Bayern dermalen betrieben wird*. Nürnberg, 1847. https://play.google.com/books/reader?id=9_pAAQAAMAAJ

12. Messerschmitt, Johann Adam. *Die bamberger Bierbrauerei*. Bamberg, 1836. https://play.google.com/books/reader?id=3TI7AAAAcAAJ

13. Herrmann, A. *Der bayerische Bierbrauer in der Malztenne, im Brauhause und Gährkeller, dann beim Gersten- und Hopfen-Einkaufe etc*. Nürnberg, 1839. https://play.google.com/books/reader?id=MQRCM1MJqfgC

14. Unger, Joseph. *Darstellung einer bayerischen Bierbrauerei.* Munich, 1846. `https://www.digitale-sammlungen.de/de/view/bsb00049117`

15. *Mittheilungen aus Baiern über das Malzen, Brauen und Gähren in Nürnberg.* J.C. Leuchs u. Compagnie, 1839. `https://play.google.com/books/reader?id=7jg7AAAAcAAJ`

16. Limmer, Leopold. *Das Ganze der bayerischen Bierbrauerei unter Angabe aller sogenannten Brau-Geheimnisse.* 1842. `https://play.google.com/books/reader?id=H5Lnpndovf8C`

17. Zierl, Lorenz. *Die bayerische Braunbier-Fabrikation und die Bier-Untersuchung durch das Fuchs'sche Hallymeter.* München, 1843. `https://play.google.com/books/reader?id=tDJCAAAAcAAJ`

18. Ziegler, Alexander. *Handbuch der gesammten Bierbrauerei.* Leipzig, 1849. `https://play.google.com/books/reader?id=DHY7AAAAcAAJ`

19. Habich, G. E. *Die Schule der Bierbrauerei.* 1863. 2. `http://reader.digitale-sammlungen.de/de/fs1/object/display/bsb11282403_00007.html`

20. Lintner, Carl. *Lehrbuch der Bierbrauerei: Nach dem heutigen Standpunkte der Theorie und Praxis unter Mitwirkung der angesehensten Theoretiker und Praktiker.* 1878. `https://babel.hathitrust.org/cgi/pt?id=uc1.31175007463857`

21. Schill, Peter. Grünmalz.. 2006. `https://commons.wikimedia.org/wiki/File:Gr%C3%BCnmalz.jpg`Licensed under CC BY-SA 2.0 DE `https://creativecommons.org/licenses/by-sa/2.0/de/deed.en`

22. Heiß, Philipp. *Die Bierbrauerei mit besonderer Berücksichtigung der Dickmaischbrauerei.* Augsburg, 1860. `https://play.google.com/books/reader?id=3Nw6AAAAcAAJ`

23. Pfauth, Hermann. *Neuestes illustrirtes Taschenbuch der Bayerischen Bierbrauerei.* Stuttgart u. Leipzig, 1870. `https://www.digitale-sammlungen.de/en/view/bsb10704296`

24. Booth, David. *The Art of Brewing.* London, 1834. `https://play.google.com/books/reader?id=9xgZAAAAYAAJ`

25. Gumbinner, Dr. Julius Ludwig. *Handbuch der praktischen Bierbrauerei nach den neuesten und bewährtesten Methoden.* Berlin, 1843. `https://play.google.com/books/reader?id=9S5FAAAAYAAJ`

26. Thausing, Julius E. *Die Theorie und Praxis der Malzbereitung und Bierfabrikation.* 3. Leipzig, 1888.

27. Dingler, Johann Gottfried (ed.). *Dinglers Polytechnisches Journal, Band 229.* 1878. `http://www.dinglr.de/volumes/pj229.html`

28. Cassian, Franz. *Die Dampfbrauerei. Eine Darstellung des gesammten Brauwesens nach dem neuesten Stande des Gewerbes.* Wien, Pest, Leipzig, 1887. `https://babel.hathitrust.org/cgi/pt?id=nyp.33433008170395`

29. Muntz, Johann Philipp Christian. *Das Bierbrauen in allen seinen Zweigen.* Neustadt a.d. Orla, 1836. `https://play.google.com/books/reader?id=qBEjZzPpeeoC`

30. Muntz, Johann Philipp Christian. *Das Bierbrauen in allen seinen Zweigen.* Plauen, 1840. `https://digital.slub-dresden.de/werkansicht/dlf/2290/4`

31. Lermer, Johann Karl. Vergleichende Untersuchung einiger renommirten Münchener Biere. *Dinglers Polytechnisches Journal.* 1866. Vol. 181, p. 134–143. `http://dinglr.de/articles/ar181037.html`

32. Prandtl, C. Untersuchungen über den Vergährungsgrad von Münchener Sommerbieren des Jahres 1867. *Dinglers Polytech-*

nisches Journal. 1868. Vol. 189, p. 397–423. http://dinglr.de/articles/ar189105.html

33. Miscellen. *Dinglers Polytechnisches Journal.* 1877. Vol. 226, p. 324. http://dinglr.de/articles/mi226mi03_8.html

34. Bieranalysen. *Dinglers Polytechnisches Journal.* 1879. Vol. 231, p. 557. http://dinglr.de/articles/mi231mi06_19.html

35. Kämmerer. *Untersuchungen in Nürnberg zum Ausschank kommender Bier und Überwachung des Flaschenbierhandels.* 1896. https://babel.hathitrust.org/cgi/pt?id=uc1.c2532473&view=1up&seq=723

36. Noback, Gustav. *Die Bier-Production in Oesterreich-Ungarn, im Deutschen Reich, in Grossbritannien und Irland, Belgien, Frankreich, den Niederlanden, Schweden und Norwegen, Russland und Nord-Amerika.* Vienna : Fromme, 1873. http://mdz-nbn-resolving.de/urn:nbn:de:bvb:12-bsb11162159-2

Index

Abmaischen, 133
Abschrecken, 172
acrospire, 26, 33, 35, 36, 38, 42, 47, 48, 51, 56, 62, 80, 86, 88, 92, 97
Ainpöckischpier, 13
airflow, 33
Amman, Hans, 12
Anlauben, 119, 133
Anschwänzen, 110, 134, 137, 143, 147
Anschwänzwasser, 123, 130, 134
ash, 21, 169
ash lye, 20
Aufmaischen, 140, 172
aufwedeln, 114
Augsburg, 152, 153, 158, 161, 163–165

Balling, 65, 139, 143, 144, 147
Bamberg, 14, 38, 49–51, 112, 166, 168–172, 175, 177, 180
barley, 7, 14, 23, 28–31, 33, 36, 39, 49
two-row, 45

barley malt, 7
Bavaria, 6, 10, 14–16, 18, 35, 98, 105, 107, 132, 153, 168, 177, 190
Old, 128, 134
Bavarian Civil Code of 1756, 15
Bavarian Code of Law of 1516, 7, 14
Bavarian Code of Law of 1616, 15
Bavarian State Regulations of 1553, 15
Bavarian State Regulations of 1616, 15
beechwood, 38, 48, 73, 82, 99
beer
    bottom-fermented, 7, 45, 48, 172, 175
    brown, 5, 7, 107, 188
    clear, 175
    dark, 84, 102
    effervescent, 37
    green, 108
    hazy, 20
    pale, 84

sour, 20, 161, 172
strong, 150
top-fermented, 48, 175, 188
white, 5, 7, 35, 89, 183, 188
white barley, 7, 185
white wheat, 7, 10, 16, 185
wine-coloured, 29
Belgium, 105
Biergrand, 162, 186, 187, 190
Biersatzregulativ, 17
Bierteig, 137
birch broom, 171
Bock, 13
Bockbier, 13, 139, 144
Bodenteig, 116
Bohemia, 11, 20, 66, 98, 105, 168
Bohemian Forest, 10
Booth, David, 116, 152
Brühbütte, 107
Braunbier, 5, 132
brewmaster, 140
brown beer, 13
brushes, 36
bunghole, 172, 187

caraway seeds, 15
cask, 107, 171, 187
    fermentation, 187
    lagering, 169
    serving, 153
cask, lagering, 118
cask, serving, 118

Cassian, Franz, 148, 150, 164, 181
cellar
    fermentation, 173
chaff, 49, 76, 90, 167
chalk, 27, 34, 38, 51, 77, 97
Closen, Barons of, 11
coal, 73, 87, 99
cockle, 18
coke, 87, 99
coolship, 106, 107, 111–113, 121, 123, 127, 131, 134, 138, 153, 155–160, 162, 163, 168, 171, 173, 174, 177, 180, 181, 183, 189
    wooden, 123
couch, 66, 76, 85, 86, 88
court brewer, 13
cow dung, 20

Dünnmaisch, 126
decoction
    thick, 105, 108, 122, 133
    thin, 105, 108
Degenberg, 10, 11
diastase, 83, 92, 149
diastatic power, 66, 149
Dickmaisch, 157
Dickmaischekochen, 106
Doppelbier, 13, 139
Dreher, Anton, 89, 116
Duke Albrecht IV., 14
Duke Albrecht V., 10
Duke Maximilian I., 11
Duke Wilhelm IV., 10

Durchschieben, 140

Eichstätt, 14
Einbeck, 13
Einmaischen, 108, 114
einschlagen, 115, 125
Einsprengen, 121
Einteigen, 114
Einweichkufe, 49
Einweichkuffe, 28, 36
endosperm, 29, 62, 65, 69–71, 80, 88, 91, 92, 97
England, 66, 76, 85, 86, 116
Englische Darre, 99
ergotamine, 20
Esel, 94

false bottom, 106, 112, 116, 122, 129, 137, 148, 152, 155, 157, 161, 163–167, 171, 172, 175, 179, 182
Farbmalz, 73, 83, 102
fermentation, 6, 81, 84, 91, 108, 118, 119, 171, 175, 187, 188
  lactic acid, 164
  primary, 108
  secondary, 119, 153, 175
  sour, 79
  spontaneous, 169
  wild, 139
fermenter, 106, 107, 153, 171
fir wood, 99
floor
  drying, 6, 26, 33, 35–38, 42–44, 47, 48, 50, 55, 60, 68, 70–72, 79, 81, 82, 89, 97, 99, 101
  growing, 24, 58
  kilning, 48, 61, 62, 82, 87, 99–101, 103
  malting, 26, 32, 33, 35, 37, 40, 42, 44, 45, 47, 49, 50, 52, 53, 55, 57, 58, 65–67, 69–72, 76, 77, 79, 80, 82, 85–88, 93–98, 101
  stone, 29, 49, 93
  storage, 44
  wooden, 29, 51, 74
flour, 80, 89
  black, coarse, 73
  grainy, 65
  malt, 171, 175
  wheat, 27, 34
  white, 61
Franconia, 112, 134, 177, 180, 181
frost, 30

Gährstoff, 173
Ganterpreis, 17, 18
germination, 24, 32, 33, 35, 37, 42, 44, 78, 86, 87, 92, 97, 99
Gerstenbütte, 62
Glasmalz, 73, 101
Glattwasser, 111, 116, 123, 128, 134, 144, 150, 177, 183
Grünmalz, 82
Grand, 109–111, 115, 120, 123, 125, 126, 130,

137, 143, 150, 156,
159, 162–165, 178,
179, 184, 189, 191
Grant, 107, 133, 154, 155
grass, 29, 37, 42, 43, 50, 68, 97
growth, 25, 29, 97
Grund, 173
gutter, 93, 114, 129, 141, 160

hacken, 115, 123, 125
Hainslein, 166, 168
Hans VI. of Degenberg, 10
Hans VIII. Sigmund of
    Degenberg, 11
Hansl, 165, 182
Hansle, 180, 181
Haufentenne, 24
Haustrunk, 113
Heiß, Philipp, 74, 134, 161,
    179, 180, 182, 188,
    190
Heinzele, 172
henbane, 15
Herrmann, A., 38, 119, 156,
    175
Hofbräuhaus, 12, 13
hop strainer, 111, 116, 121,
    123, 127, 131, 134,
    138, 183
Hopfenrösten, 168, 182
hops, 7, 14, 17, 20, 118, 123,
    126, 131, 133, 138,
    148, 158, 162, 168,
    171, 173, 174, 179,
    181, 185
    Bavarian, 20, 117
    Bohemian, 20, 117, 168

    country-side, 131, 191
    fine quality, 143
    Franconian, 168
    Hallertauer, 143
    high-quality, 183
    medium-quality, 143
    new, 127, 155
    old, 127, 155
    Saazer, 132, 143
    Spalter, 132, 143
    spent, 116, 127, 152, 172,
        177
husk, 29, 30, 40, 43, 50, 52,
    57, 58, 61, 62, 64, 65,
    69, 77, 80, 88, 90, 92,
    97, 102

isinglass, 21

juniper berries, 15

Kühlgeläger, 131
Kelheim, 190
kesselroth, 173
kettle, 107, 110, 115, 117,
    119–121, 152, 154,
    156, 157, 165
kiln, 29, 36, 73
    air, 99, 100
    double, 99–101
    English, 99
    hot-air, 48, 73, 82
    smoke, 82, 99
kilning, 26, 28, 30, 34, 35, 38,
    42–44, 48, 50, 51,
    60–62, 72–74, 81–83,
    96, 99–102

Koffent, 166

Läutermaische, 162
Läuterungsmaisch, 172, 173
lactic acid, 143, 164, 165
Lagerbier, 7, 13, 17, 45, 47, 121, 124, 126, 132, 136–139, 144, 146, 153–158, 160, 161, 171, 180
Landshut, 14
lauter tun, 147, 150
Lautermaisch, 109, 126, 179, 189
Lautermaische, 115, 120, 130, 133
Lautermeisch, 178
Lettl, Sigmund, 12
Leuchs, J.C., 45, 153
Liesing, 89
Limmer, Leopold, 49
Lintner, Carl, 144, 163
Lower Bavaria, 10
Luftdarre, 82, 99
Luftmalz, 35, 60, 72, 89, 99

Mänhart, Georg, 13
Märzenbier, 16, 171, 175
Märzenbierlosung, 16
Müller, P., 62, 105, 132
Maischschaufel, 108
malt, 27, 139
    air-dried, 29, 48, 74, 84, 90, 99
    barley, 5, 35
    colour, 73, 83, 102
    crushed, 80, 108, 134, 149, 154, 156, 158, 161, 175, 182
    dark, 84
    finely ground, 152
    glass, 73, 101
    green, 82, 101
    kilned, 34, 83, 89
    pale barley, 183, 188
    pale wheat, 183, 188
    roasted, 73
    stone, 27, 44, 55, 73, 101
    wheat, 5, 35
malting floor, 32
Malzaufschlag, 17
marble, 93
mash, 90
    decoction, 105
    scorched, 141
    thick, 109, 120, 125, 136, 142, 149, 151, 164
    thin, 109, 133, 151, 156, 158
    triple decoction, 113, 185
mash paddle, 124, 139, 172, 179
mash tun, 107, 115, 119, 122, 124, 125, 133, 150, 152, 153, 155, 156, 161, 162, 170, 178
Messerschmitt, Johann Adam, 36, 172, 174
Meyer, Friedrich, 30, 113, 123, 158, 177, 183, 185

Michaelmas, 6, 16
Munich, 13, 14, 16, 47, 57–60, 62, 66, 116, 132, 134, 150, 151
Muntz, Johann Philipp Christian, 170

Nachbier, 110, 111, 113, 115, 116, 120, 123, 126–128, 131, 133, 134, 137, 138, 156, 158, 166, 168, 169, 174, 177, 180, 181
Nachbierkühle, 134
Nachbierpfanne, 127
Nachguss, 137, 138, 145
Nachweiche, 66, 76
Notwirt, 16
Nuremberg, 13, 14, 45, 47, 48, 153, 158, 161, 163

Oberknecht, 115
Oberteig, 111, 112, 116, 123, 127, 128, 134, 146, 158
oil, 169
    aromatic, 123
    ethereal, 138
    hop, 155

Paulaner, 13, 47
peat, 73, 99
Pfaff, 148, 154, 161, 163, 166, 167, 171–173, 175, 178
Pfaffe, 106, 159, 160, 179
Pfaffen, 182

Pfannenknecht, 115, 129
Pfauth, Hermann, 90, 139
pine wood, 99
pitch, 153, 171
poison darnel, 18
pot ash, 21
Prague, 66, 87
pre-masher, 149, 151
Prince-elector Maximilian I. Joseph of Bavaria, 16
privy council of Bavaria, 20
protein, 36, 42, 92, 131, 136, 144, 165
purity law, 14

Quellbottich, 51
Quellkasten, 56, 74
quicklime, 21

Rauchdarre, 82, 99
Regensburg, 14
Reinheitsgebot, 14
Rohrdarre, 73
rootlets, 25, 26, 29, 30, 32, 33, 35–38, 40–42, 45–51, 54, 56, 59–62, 65–72, 74, 78, 80, 86, 89, 92, 95, 96, 98, 99, 102, 103

saccharometer, 151
Saccharomyces cerevisiae, 6
Saccharomyces eubayanus, 6
salt, 15, 21, 153
Salvator, 14, 139
Salvatorbier, 13

Sarg, 107
Satzbrauen, 48, 153, 158, 164, 188
Saxony, 13
Schöps, 131, 150
Schankpreis, 17, 18
Scharl, Benno, 23, 107
Schenkbier, 7, 16, 17, 121, 123, 126, 129–132, 137–139, 144, 146, 153–158, 160, 161, 178, 179
Schottisches Drehkreuz, 147
Schwarzenberg, 10
Schwechat, 89
Schwelge, 26
Schwelke, 55
Scotland, 54, 116
Sedlmayr, Gabriel, 76, 116, 134
Seifert, Johann Albert Joseph, 28, 166
shovel, 32, 38, 41, 50, 79, 93, 94, 152, 156, 159, 161, 174
Silesia, 98
slate, 172
Sommerbier, 7, 16, 124, 126, 129–131, 136–139, 141, 143, 144, 148, 158, 160, 162, 164, 173, 178, 180, 183
Spaten, 76, 134
St. George's Day, 6
starch, 25, 26, 68, 83, 91, 92, 102, 141, 155, 163

steam engine, 150
Steinmalz, 27, 44, 55, 73, 101
strainer, 163
straw, 166, 169
sulphur, 171
Sumpf, 166
Swabia, 134
sweat, 24, 25, 32, 41, 45, 46, 59–61, 67, 95, 96, 98
  cold, 59, 66, 98
  warm, 99

Tölz, 16
tannin, 138
thermometer, 38, 78, 125, 169
Träber, 128
Trockenboden, 55
Trub, 144

Überziehrinne, 114
Unterholzer, 13
Unterteig, 112, 116, 123, 134
Upper Bavaria, 14
Upper Palatinate, 11

vessel
  brewing, 106, 126, 151
  fermentation, 169
  fermenting, 118, 169
  open, 166
  post-steeping, 76
  steeping, 36, 38, 49, 56, 57, 62, 74, 75, 85, 87, 90, 98
  stone, 64
Vienna, 89, 116
vinegar, 35, 89, 123, 127

wine, 89

Würzbütte, 107

Wachstenne, 24

water, 7, 14, 20, 23–25, 28, 30, 31, 35, 36, 38, 39, 45, 49–52, 56–58, 60, 62–66, 74–76, 80, 85–87, 90–93, 96, 98, 101, 106–111, 113–129, 131–135, 137, 139–154, 156–159, 161–164, 166–168, 171–175, 177–179, 181–186, 188, 190, 191
- cold, 108, 175
- hard, 20, 31, 39, 64, 91
- hot, 111
- rain, 166
- river, 166
- soft, 20, 28, 31, 64, 91
- well, 166, 174

Weißbier, 5, 6

Weißbierhefe, 6

Weiche, 23, 27, 30, 51, 62, 63, 74

Weichkasten, 56

Welke, 26, 55

wheat

winter, 35

wine, 119

Winterbier, 7, 108, 113, 119, 123, 126, 131, 137–139, 141, 143, 144, 148, 158, 160, 162, 173, 179, 180, 183

Wittelsbacher, 11

Wolf, Peter, 12

wort, 70, 90, 118, 123, 133, 138
- sweet, 108

yeast, 7, 153, 169, 187, 189
- bottom-fermenting, 6, 169, 170
- brewer's, 6
- dried, 169
- harvested, 111
- top-cropped, 170, 171
- top-cropping, 6
- top-fermenting, 6, 187
- white beer, 6, 185
- wild, 6

Zacherl, 14, 47

Ziegler, Alexander, 56, 128

Zierl, Lorenz, 51, 121

Zschopau, 13

Printed in Great Britain
by Amazon